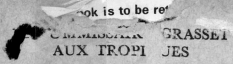

COMMISSAIRE GRASSET
AUX TROPIQUES

Other French readers

LE COMMISSAIRE GRASSET AUX TROPIQUES

★

By

RICHARD MUSMAN, M.A.

Formerly Head of the Modern Languages Department,
Bedales School, Petersfield

Illustrations by
LEWIS STRINGER

BELL & HYMAN
LONDON

Published by
BELL & HYMAN LIMITED
Denmark House
37–39 Queen Elizabeth Street
London SE1 2QB

First Published in 1966 by
G. Bell & Sons Ltd
Reprinted 1969, 1973, 1979, 1980

ISBN 0 7135 0771 3

PRINTED IN GREAT BRITAIN BY OFFSET LITHOGRAPHY BY
BILLING AND SONS LTD., GUILDFORD, LONDON AND WORCESTER

INTRODUCTION

In *Grasset aux Tropiques* Grasset and his favourite inspector, Lapuce, tackle a case which takes them to the tropical islands of Martinique and Tahiti. This third book of the Grasset series is a straightforward suspense story in which the situations and characters are not as improbable or farcical as in the first two books.

The story is told in the past, and the book is intended for those who have already learned the Passé Composé and Imperfect tenses. The Vocabulary and syntax are straightforward and simple. Idioms which might prove difficult are explained in the Notes at the end of each chapter, and in order to encourage fluent reading less common words, and words whose meaning might not be easy to deduce, have been translated in footnotes. There are maps of Martinique and French Polynesia and a number of explanatory notes.

My grateful thanks once more to M. Jacques Gachet, Mrs. Huguette Foster and to my wife for their invaluable help.

RICHARD MUSMAN

CONTENTS

1   LA CHINOISE BLONDE

Le bateau approchait de Calais. Les passagers montaient sur le pont, suivis de matelots qui portaient leurs bagages.   Grasset, assis sur sa valise, fumait sa pipe et regardait.   'C'est une invasion', se disait-il en souriant.

Un groupe de jeunes Anglaises, dont quelques-unes étaient très jolies, passait devant lui.   Elles bavardaient, riaient, ouvraient leurs sacs pour chercher leurs passeports, leurs billets de débarquement, leurs bâtons de rouge.[1]   Elles allaient passer leurs vacances en France, à Paris, au bord de la mer, à la montagne.   Elles allaient essayer de parler français, comme lui avait essayé* de parler anglais.

Le Commissaire Grasset revenait de Londres où il avait fait une enquête[2] sur la disparition d'un diplomate français.   Il n'avait pas pu éclaircir le mystère, mais il avait fort bien dîné chez son ami, l'Inspecteur Scrubs de Scotland Yard.   Il était de bonne humeur.

Le bateau est entré au port.   Grasset a mis sa pipe dans sa poche et s'est levé.   Il se baissait pour prendre sa valise quand soudain il a remarqué qu'une des jeunes Anglaises le regardait fixement.   Elle avait les cheveux blonds et elle était très mince, comme toutes les Anglaises, mais, ce qui était très curieux, elle avait les yeux en amande.[3]   'Une petite Chinoise blonde!' pensait Grasset.

A ce moment-là la petite 'Chinoise blonde' lui a souri, et Grasset, galant comme toujours, lui a retourné le compliment.   'Mais qu'est-ce qu'elle veut? se

---

[1] lipstick   [2] enquiry   [3] almond-shaped

disait-il. Les jeunes filles n'ont pas l'habitude de sourire à de vieux croulants* comme moi!'

Le bateau s'est arrêté. Grasset s'est dirigé lentement vers la passerelle de service,[1] marchant derrière le groupe de jeunes Anglaises, et tout à coup il a eu l'impression que la petite 'Chinoise blonde' l'attendait, qu'elle voulait être près de lui. Elle n'avait pas de bagages, mais elle avait à la main un grand sac de cuir noir qu'elle serrait contre elle comme si elle avait peur de le perdre. 'C'est curieux, se disait Grasset, en descendant sur le quai. Il y a plus de gendarmes que d'habitude.'

Il était évident que la 'Chinoise blonde' les avait remarqués elle aussi, parce qu'elle s'était arrêtée et Grasset voyait qu'elle était pâle comme la mort.

Ce sont les jeunes Anglaises qui ont débarqué les premières. Une fois sur le quai elles se sont dirigées tout de suite vers le train qui attendait. Mais les gendarmes les ont arrêtées, leur disant qu'elles devaient passer à la Douane.[2] 'C'est curieux, se disait Grasset. D'habitude on visite les bagages dans le train.'

Les jeunes Anglaises ont obéi sans faire aucune objection, mais la 'Chinoise blonde' a regardé autour d'elle comme si elle voulait se sauver. Puis elle a vu que Grasset la regardait et elle lui a souri timidement.

—Vous n'avez rien à craindre, mademoiselle, a dit Grasset pour l'encourager. Les douaniers français sont toujours très gentils avec les étrangères, surtout si elles sont jeunes et jolies.

—Mais monsieur, a-t-elle répondu. Je ne suis pas étrangère. C'est ma première visite en France, mais je suis Française et j'ai un passeport français.

Puis elle a ajouté, 'Vous allez à Paris, monsieur?'

[1] gangway   [2] Customs

—Oui, a répondu Grasset.

Ils sont arrivés enfin à la Douane où des douzaines de douaniers et de gendarmes attendaient.

—Ouvrez, mesdemoiselles, ouvrez, ouvrez!

Les jeunes Anglaises ont dû ouvrir leurs valises, leurs sacs, leurs bâtons de rouge, et même leurs montres. C'était un spectacle extraordinaire. Grasset n'avait jamais vu une chose pareille. Un douanier s'est approché de la 'Chinoise blonde', a pris tout de suite son sac et l'a ouvert sans même lui demander si elle avait quelque chose à déclarer.

—Votre montre, mademoiselle!

—Je n'ai pas de montre, monsieur.

—Vous ne portez jamais de montre? a demandé soudain le douanier, lui prenant* la main gauche.

—Si, a balbutié la jeune fille, quelquefois, mais je . . . je l'ai perdue.

Le gendarme a fait venir une femme en uniforme.

—Fouillez[1]-la!

La femme a emmené la 'Chinoise blonde' et le douanier s'est tourné vers Grasset.

—Mais qu'est-ce qui se passe? a demandé Grasset, lui montrant sa carte d'identité.

—Je n'ai pas le droit de vous le dire, Monsieur le Commissaire. C'est. . . .

—Bah! a grommelé Grasset.

Puis il est allé à la recherche de sa place réservée dans le rapide de Paris.

*   *   *

Grasset a allumé sa pipe et s'est mis à lire le *Times* qu'il avait acheté à la Gare Victoria. Une heure plus tard le train n'avait pas encore quitté la gare maritime.

[1] fouiller, to search

Grasset était sur le point de redescendre sur le quai quand soudain il a entendu des chuchotements[1] sous la fenêtre de son compartiment.   C'était la 'Chinoise blonde' qui parlait à un homme dont il ne pouvait pas voir le visage.   Mais il y avait* dans la personne de cet individu quelque chose de singulier, de sinistre même, et soudain Grasset s'est aperçu[2] qu'il avait le bras droit plus court que le gauche.

Un employé* a crié, 'En voiture!'*   La 'Chinoise blonde' a quitté brusquement son compagnon et est montée aussitôt dans le train.   L'homme, sans se retourner, est parti en courant dans la direction de la ville.

—Attention au départ!*

Le train s'est mis en marche.   Dans le compartiment où se trouvait Grasset il y avait deux hommes d'affaires et une jeune Suissesse[3] tenant un gros bébé sur les genoux.   Au bout de deux minutes le bébé s'est mis à pleurer.   La mère s'est excusée en rougissant.

—Ce sont ses dents, vous comprenez, messieurs. Si vous voulez. . . .

—Oh, ne vous dérangez pas, madame, je vous en prie, a répondu Grasset.

Tout à coup, en levant les yeux, il a vu dans le couloir la 'Chinoise blonde' qui le regardait.   Leurs regards se sont croisés et elle lui a souri.   Puis elle est entrée dans le compartiment et s'est assise à côté de lui.

—Je viens vous demander de me rendre ma montre, monsieur, a-t-elle soufflé.

—Comment? s'est écrié Grasset très surpris.

—Oui, monsieur, vous ne l'avez pas trouvée? Je l'ai mise dans votre poche à la Douane.   J'ai eu peur des douaniers.   Vous aviez l'air si gentil, monsieur. . . .

---

[1] whispering   [2] *s'apercevoir*, to notice   [3] Swiss woman

Grasset a mis la main dans sa poche

Grasset a mis la main dans sa poche. La montre était là! Lui, le célèbre Commissaire Grasset, l'avait passée en contrebande! Cette pensée l'a fait sourire, mais il a remarqué que la jeune fille ne souriait pas. Ses yeux en amande n'avaient plus l'air innocent d'une petite fille timide. Ils ressemblaient plutôt à ceux d'un serpent. Grasset a sorti la main de sa poche.

—Vous plaisantez, n'est-ce pas, mademoiselle? Il n'y a pas de montre dans ma poche.

La 'Chinoise blonde' s'est levée furieuse.

—Alors je me suis trompée. Vous n'êtes pas gentil. Vous êtes un voleur!

Les deux Anglais, qui avaient le nez fourré[1] dans leur *Daily Telegraph*, ont levé la tête.

—Aoh! se sont-ils exclamés en regardant sévèrement Grasset.

La 'Chinoise blonde' s'est tournée vers eux.

—Messieurs, ce monsieur a ma montre, je vous assure.

—Aoh yes? ont répondu les Anglais sans bouger.

—Ce petit contrebandier se trompe, a expliqué Grasset en souriant. Elle a voulu cacher sa montre dans ma poche, mais par erreur elle l'a laissée tomber par terre.

—Vous mentez, monsieur, a crié la jeune fille de plus en plus furieuse. Laissez-moi voir!

A ce moment le contrôleur est arrivé.

—Vos billets, s'il vous plaît, messieurs-dames.

Grasset, les deux Anglais et la jeune Suissesse ont tendu leurs billets au contrôleur. La 'Chinoise blonde' lui a tourné le dos, comme si elle n'avait pas entendu.

—Votre billet, mademoiselle.

—Je l'ai perdu. . . . C'est combien?

[1] buried

—Suivez-moi, mademoiselle, a répondu le contrôleur, sortant du compartiment.

—Bonnes vacances! lui a lancé Grasset en riant.

—A bientôt! a crié la 'Chinoise blonde' sur un ton
furieux.

Les deux Anglais se sont retirés derrière leurs
journaux. Grasset a bourré une sixième pipe. Le
bébé suisse a pleuré sans cesse... et le train roulait à
toute vitesse vers Paris.

NOTES

avait essayé ... était arrivé: *had tried ... had arrived*
(*happened*).   This tense is called the Pluperfect and is
made up of the Past Participle and the Imperfect of
avoir or **être.**

croulants: *dead-beats.*   The literal meaning is 'crumbling'.
The word is sometimes used by teenagers to describe
middle-aged people.

lui prenant la main gauche: *taking hold of her left hand.*

**il y avait dans la personne de cet individu quelque
chose de singulier:** *there was something strange about
this individual.*

employé: employee, but here *railway official.*   There is no
exact English equivalent.

En voiture! (*into the carriage*) is a warning to passengers to
take their seats.   **Attention au départ!** (*beware of
the departure*) is shouted just as the train is about to
leave.

En descendant du train à la Gare du Nord* Grasset a vu la 'Chinoise blonde' qui parlait à deux hommes à la barrière.   Il a fait semblant[2] de ne pas les remarquer, espérant les voir de plus près.   Mais à son approche ils se sont sauvés tous les trois.   'Ils ne savent pas qui je suis, se disait-il. Alors ils vont certainement me suivre.'

Il a donc décidé de ne pas rentrer chez lui et a dit au chauffeur de son taxi de le conduire à un petit hôtel proche de son appartement.   Cet hôtel, dont il connaissait bien le patron, était situé à une centaine de mètres de la Seine.   On n'avait qu'à* tourner le coin et on pouvait voir les fenêtres de la P.J.*

Le patron, petit homme jovial, a été très surpris de voir son ami.

—Qu'est-ce qui t'amène?   Est-ce que tu viens me dire qu'on va commettre un meurtre chez moi ce soir? Tu. . . .

—C'est possible, a interrompu Grasset gravement.

—Excellent!   Qui, par exemple?

—Moi!

—Bravo! s'est écrié le patron en riant.

—Écoute!   Je ne plaisante pas.

Puis Grasset a raconté à son ami tout ce qui lui était arrivé depuis son arrivée à Calais.

—Je suis certain qu'on va me rendre visite cette nuit. Si quelqu'un vient se renseigner sur moi, il faut lui dire que je m'appelle Georges Martin, que je suis un homme

_____

[1] spies   [2] *faire semblant de*, to pretend

d'affaires et que je suis à Paris pour quatre jours . . . et
donne le numéro de ma chambre. . . . Quelle chambre
vas-tu me donner?

—La meilleure, mon vieux, celle que j'appelle la
'chambre des espions'.

—Pourquoi 'les espions'?

—A cause de l'armoire. Un de mes clients . . .
c'est arrivé pendant la guerre . . . y a fait deux petits
trous juste au niveau des yeux.

—C'est parfait. Je monte* tout de suite. Télé-
phone-moi si tu as des nouvelles. A tout à l'heure.

La 'chambre des espions' était située au deuxième
étage et donnait sur la rue. Pas de balcon, pas
d'escalier de secours,[1] pas de tuyaux[2] près de la fenêtre.
'Alors ce sera par la porte qu'on viendra m'assassiner',
s'est dit Grasset.

Puis, s'asseyant sur le lit, il a sorti la montre de sa
poche. C'était une montre très ordinaire, bien que
assez grande pour une femme. Mais ce qui l'a frappé
tout de suite, c'est qu'elle était extrêmement légère et
qu'elle ne marchait pas. Il a pris son canif et l'a
ouverte.

—Tiens! s'est-il écrié.

Dans le boîtier il y avait un petit rouleau de papier
très mince. Il l'a déroulé avec soin. Le papier était
couvert de lettres et de chiffres.

—Pas mal! s'est-il dit, tendant la main vers le
téléphone qui se trouvait sur la table de chevet.[3] Il a
décroché le récepteur, a appelé la P.J. et a demandé à
parler à son inspecteur favori, le petit Lapuce.

—Dis donc, petit, qu'est-ce qu'on espérait trouver
ce matin à Calais? Tu comprends ce que je veux dire?
. . . Bon! Alors c'est une question d'espionnage? Je

---

[1] fire-escape   [2] *le tuyau*, pipe   [3] bedside table

2

vois! Alors, écoute-moi bien. Moi, j'étais à Calais ce matin, tu comprends? Je suis sur la piste de. . . . Je n'ai pas le temps de t'expliquer maintenant, mais je suis en ce moment à l'Hôtel Saint Jérome. Tu le connais, n'est-ce pas? . . . Quartier Latin.* C'est ça. Eh bien, quelqu'un va me rendre visite ce soir . . . entre minuit et quatre heures du matin, je crois. Ma chambre est au deuxième étage, fenêtre de gauche. N'empêche pas ce personnage d'entrer. Il aura sans doute un passe-partout.[1] Mais quand il sortira, suis-le. . . . Comment? . . . Oui, c'est ça. A demain, petit, et bonne chance.

Deux minutes plus tard le patron a téléphoné pour lui dire qu'un homme venait de se présenter à la réception[2] disant qu'il était de la P.J. et qu'il voulait voir toutes les fiches,* surtout celle du dernier venu.

—C'était toi, le dernier venu, mon vieux!

—Bon! a dit Grasset. Je dînerai dans ma chambre. Monte-moi un bon bifteck bien garni.

*   *   *

Après dîner il a demandé au patron une feuille de papier semblable à celui du rouleau. Puis il a copié les lettres et les chiffres, mais en les changeant et les mélangeant un peu. Après quoi il a mis le rouleau dans son portefeuille, le remplaçant dans la montre par la copie. Ensuite il a posé la montre sur la table à côté du téléphone, s'est assis dans le fauteuil et a allumé sa pipe.

Vers minuit il s'est levé et est allé à la fenêtre. La rue était déserte. Est-ce que Lapuce était déjà là, caché dans l'encadrement de quelque porte? Il a

---

[1] skeleton key   [2] hotel reception desk

soupiré. Il savait qu'il courait un grand risque, que si l'on avait l'intention de le tuer, il ne pourrait* pas se défendre. Mais il s'était décidé. A minuit précis il s'est déshabillé et s'est mis au lit. Il avait renoncé à l'idée de se cacher dans l'armoire. 'Que penserait* notre ami, se disait-il, s'il ne me trouvait pas au lit à deux heures du matin?'

Il ne voulait pas éveiller les soupçons. Il n'était plus le célèbre Commissaire Grasset. Il était Georges Martin, homme d'affaires. 'On s'assurera que le papier est toujours là. On prendra la montre. Puis on partira. On ne me tuera pas. Du moins, je l'espère!'

Trois heures se sont écoulées. Il a eu de la peine à ne pas s'endormir. Puis enfin, à trois heures du matin, il a entendu un léger bruit, comme si quelqu'un marchait sur la pointe des pieds dans le couloir. Le moment d'après la porte s'est ouverte sans bruit et le rayon d'une lampe électrique a éclairé le lit. 'Allons! se disait Grasset. C'est peut-être ma dernière heure!'

Il s'était mis à ronfler[1] légèrement, et il n'osait pas ouvrir les yeux. Mais vingt secondes plus tard il savait que l'étranger était tout près du lit, car il pouvait l'entendre respirer. Il était presque certain que c'était un homme, un homme qui, en outre, avait l'habitude de pénétrer dans des chambres au beau milieu de la nuit. 'Il est en train d'examiner la montre pour s'assurer que le message est toujours là,' se disait Grasset.

Au bout d'une minute l'étranger a poussé un soupir de soulagement,[2] et s'est dirigé vers la porte. La porte s'est refermée. Le bruit de pas dans le couloir a bientôt cessé, et en ouvrant les yeux Grasset a vu que la montre n'était plus sur la table. Il a sauté à bas du

---

[1] to snore   [2] relief

L'étranger était tout près du lit

lit et est allé à la fenêtre.   De l'autre côté de la rue un homme . . . Lapuce, sans doute . . . est sorti de l'encadrement d'une porte et a disparu dans la direction des quais.   Grasset est retourné au lit et s'est endormi aussitôt.

A huit heures et demie il s'est rendu au Quai des Orfèvres.   Voyant que Lapuce n'était pas encore revenu, le Commissaire est allé voir son chef.

—Nous avons eu de la chance, a dit celui-ci, regardant le rouleau que Grasset lui avait donné.   Quelqu'un, nous ne savons pas qui, a téléphoné à Scotland Yard trois heures après votre départ de Londres.   Ce personnage disait qu'une jeune femme allait essayer de faire passer en France quelque chose d'extrêmement important.   Il refusait de dire ce que c'était et il ne savait pas à quel port la femme allait débarquer.

—De quoi s'agit-il* à votre avis ? a demandé Grasset.

—Il s'agit d'une bande d'espions internationaux, sans aucun doute.   Ce que vous venez de trouver est peut-être la formule d'une fusée[1] ou de quelque arme secrète.   Nous croyons maintenant que notre diplomate disparu avait découvert quelque chose et que c'est pour cela qu'il a été kidnappé . . . ou assassiné.

—Si vous permettez, a dit Grasset, je vais aller voir si Lapuce est revenu.   Il aura certainement des nouvelles.

Lapuce l'attendait dans son bureau.   Il chantait et faisait semblant de jouer de la guitare.

—Mais qu'as-tu ? s'est écrié Grasset étonné.

—J'ai toujours rêvé d'aller à Tahiti,* patron, a répondu Lapuce en riant.

—Comment ?   Es-tu fou ?

—Non, patron.   Vous allez voir.

[1] rocket

NOTES

La Gare du Nord: Paris station serving the north of France and the Channel ports, Calais, Boulogne and Dunkerque.

on n'avait qu'à: *one had only to.*

P.J.: Police Judiciaire, the French equivalent of Scotland Yard. It is situated on the Quai des Orfèvres, very close to the Cathedral of Notre-Dame.

je monte: *I'll go up.* When the French want to express the *immediate* future they use the Present Tense.

Quartier Latin: *Latin Quarter,* situated on the left bank of the Seine and centred around the Sorbonne. It is the student quarter of Paris.

fiches: *registration cards.* These cards, demanding name, address, occupation, passport number etc. must—by law—be filled in by all hotel guests on arrival.

ne pourrait pas . . . que penserait notre ami?: *would not be able . . . what would our friend think?* This tense is called the conditional and it is formed by taking the future stem of any verb, regular or irregular (e.g. **penser-, pourr-**) and adding the imperfect endings.

De quoi s'agit-il?: *What's it (all) about?*

Tahiti: This South Sea island is described in the Note on p. 40.

3   LAPUCE 'SE MARIE'

—Vous avez eu raison de me poster devant l'hôtel, patron, a commencé Lapuce. Nous sommes sur la piste de quelque chose qui va nous mener peut-être aux quatre coins du monde. Mais je commencerai par le commencement. . . . Notre homme . . . je n'ai jamais vu quelqu'un d'aussi bizarre. Il avait le bras droit plus court que le gauche. . . . Notre homme a utilisé un passe-partout pour entrer à l'hôtel. C'est certainement un professionel! Mais j'ai eu l'impression qu'il n'était pas armé et que vous n'étiez pas en danger. . . . Je suppose qu'il a trouvé sans difficulté ce qu'il cherchait?

Grasset a fait signe que oui.

—En tout cas il a reparu au bout de cinq minutes, a continué Lapuce. Une voiture l'attendait au coin de la rue. J'avais laissé la mienne dans la rue voisine.

Grasset s'était assis à son bureau et bourrait sa pipe. Il avait l'air très content.

—Eh bien, c'était difficile, vous comprenez, patron. A cette heure les rues sont désertes. Je savais qu'il allait s'effrayer s'il croyait que quelqu'un le suivait. Alors j'ai dû le suivre sans être vu. Heureusement sa voiture était vieille et faisait beaucoup de bruit, tandis que la mienne, la D.S.* . . .

—Sois bref, petit, a interrompu Grasset.

—Notre homme a traversé la Seine, patron, puis s'est dirigé vers le Marais.* Je ne sais pas pourquoi, mais j'étais presque sûr qu'il avait rendez-vous avec quelqu'un Place des Vosges.* J'avais raison. Sa voiture s'est arrêtée à quelques pas de la Maison de Victor Hugo.* L'homme a disparu sous les arcades, mais il n'était pas difficile de deviner dans quelle maison il était entré. Il était trois heures du matin. Tout le monde dormait. Il n'y avait pas de lumière aux fenêtres . . . à l'exception d'une seule au deuxième étage. J'ai laissé ma voiture de l'autre côté de la place et me suis dirigé vers la lumière. Comme il faisait très chaud, la fenêtre était ouverte et les rideaux n'étaient pas tirés. J'avais mon passe-partout, mais je n'ai pas osé entrer par la porte. C'est alors que j'ai remarqué qu'il y avait à côté un immeuble[1] inoccupé.

—Et tu t'es servi de ton passe-partout pour y entrer! a interrompu Grasset. Tu es monté jusqu'au deuxième étage, tu as ouvert très doucement la fenêtre et tu as écouté!

—C'est ça, patron!

Grasset a souri.

—Tu sais que c'est défendu? Qu'est-ce que tu aurais fait si un agent t'avait vu? Mais continue, petit. Ce que tu me racontes est bien intéressant.

—D'abord je n'ai rien compris. En fait je croyais que mes voisins parlaient une langue étrangère. En tout cas ils parlaient à voix basse. Mais soudain quelqu'un . . . il avait un fort accent américain . . . s'est emporté,[2] et je n'oublierai jamais ce qu'il disait. C'était comme si j'assistais à une scène d'un film de James Bond. 'Votre premier "job" pour l'Organisation Fantôme n'a pas réussi, ma chère. Je ne sais pas ce que dira votre père.' Puis une voix de femme a répondu, 'Mais c'est vous que mon père blâmera. Vous ne m'aviez pas avertie que quelqu'un nous avait dénoncés à la police. Du reste, est-ce que je savais,

---

[1] house   [2] *s'emporter*, to lose one's temper

moi, que ce gros papa était un voleur? Il avait l'air si
innocent, bête même.' . . . Mais qu'avez-vous, patron?

—Rien, a grommelé Grasset. Continue. Le gros
Papa t'écoute!

—Ah! je comprends. Pardon, patron! . . . Alors
la femme a protesté que ce n'était pas grave puisqu'on
avait retrouvé la montre et que la formule y était
toujours. . . . Ce n'était pas la vraie, n'est-ce pas,
patron?

—Non! Continue.

—Eh bien, votre petite amie a affirmé qu'il y avait un
traître dans l'Organisation et qu'il fallait le trouver
tout de suite. Quel drame, patron! Il y a eu un
silence. Puis une autre voix a dit, 'Ce n'est plus
nécessaire. C'était Radotski. Il est mort.' Après
quoi il y a eu tant de bruit que je n'ai entendu qu'une
partie de ce qu'ils disaient.

—Combien de ces messieurs y avait-il?

—Quatre, y compris.[1] . . .

—La Chinoise blonde! a interrompu Grasset.

—Comment?

—Rien. Je t'expliquerai plus tard. Continue.

—Ils avaient tous des accents étrangers, à l'exception
de. . . .

—La Chinoise blonde, a encore interrompu Grasset.
Continue.

—J'arrive maintenant au plus important, patron, et
c'est *très* important, je vous assure. La bande part ce
soir par Air France . . . ou pour la Martinique,* ou
pour Tahiti. Je ne peux pas vous dire où. Ils
parlaient tous ensemble. Mais j'ai l'impression que
l'Organisation Fantôme a deux cachettes dont l'une
est à la Martinique et l'autre à Tahiti.

[1] including

MARTINIQUE

10 kms

Grasset a réfléchi un moment, la main sur le téléphone.

—Nous sommes aujourd'hui jeudi, n'est-ce pas?

Puis il a décroché le récepteur et a appelé Air France.

—Pas d'avion pour Tahiti ce soir, petit, a-t-il annoncé en raccrochant. Mais il y en a un qui part pour la Martinique à 23 heures 15.

—Qu'est-ce que nous allons faire, patron?

—Emprunter un avion à réaction[1] à l'Armée de l'Air. Nous partons le plus tôt possible pour les Antilles.[2] J'aienvie de parler au père de ma petite Chinoise blonde.

*   *   *

L'avion à réaction a atterri au Lamentin, l'aéroport de l'île, trois heures avant l'arrivée de l'avion d'Air France. Un inspecteur créole, l'Inspecteur Diamant, attendait sur la piste.

—Je suis à vos ordres, Monsieur le Commissaire. Je viens de parler au téléphone à votre chef.   Il paraît que c'est grave.

—C'est bien probable, a grommelé Grasset. Mais j'ai soif, moi.   Ce maudit réacteur. . . !

—Si vous voulez bien m'accompagner à Fort-de-France,* Monsieur le Commissaire, a proposé l'inspecteur.   C'est tout près.   Nous avons assez de temps. Là je vous offrirai un verre de notre fameux rhum.

Alors Grasset et Lapuce sont montés dans la voiture de l'inspecteur qui les a conduits tout de suite à la charmante petite capitale de l'île.   Ils ont passé devant la statue de l'Impératrice Joséphine* et se sont arrêtés enfin devant une belle terrasse qui donnait sur la magnifique baie.

[1] jet (plane)   [2] West Indies

Une jolie serveuse leur a apporté trois verres de rhum

—Mais c'est épatant! s'est écrié Lapuce.

—Pas mal, a grogné Grasset.   Mais ce rhum. . . .

Ils se sont assis sous une immense ombrelle orangée et une jolie serveuse leur a apporté trois verres de rhum.

—Il est bon, votre rhum, a remarqué Grasset.

—C'est le meilleur du monde, a répondu l'inspecteur, très fier.   Puis il y a eu un silence pendant que Grasset regardait la mer bleue et les montagnes qui s'élevaient de l'autre côté de la baie.   Il rêvait et les deux inspecteurs n'osaient pas interrompre ses rêves.   Mais enfin il s'est tourné vers Lapuce.

—Tu devras être là quand l'avion atterrira, et pour cela il te faudra te déguiser en Créole.   Tu as l'air d'un flic[1]!

—Et vous, patron?

—Moi, petit?   Je suis trop vieux pour me déguiser. En tout cas ma petite Chinoise blonde reconnaîtrait son gros Papa, même s'il se déguisait en Créole.

—Eh bien, que voulez-vous. . .?

Soudain l'Inspecteur Diamant a éclaté de rire.   Puis il a crié, 'Marie!'   Une belle Créole assise à une table voisine s'est levée et s'est approchée.   Elle était accompagnée de deux petites filles.

—Je vous présente ma sœur, Madame Perle, a dit l'Inspecteur Diamant.

Grasset et Lapuce se sont levés.

—Enchanté, madame.

Madame Perle, qui était vraiment très belle, portait deux énormes boucles d'oreilles en topaze et une robe écarlate.   Ses deux petites filles étaient habillées de bleu.

—Ma sœur est arrivée hier de la Guadeloupe,* a continué l'Inspecteur Diamant.   Elle va passer ses

[1] cop

vacances chez moi.   Personne à la Martinique ne la connaît.   Son mari appartient à la Police de la Guadeloupe.   Alors elle connaît le métier.[1]   Je peux la prêter à l'Inspecteur Lapuce.

—Tu as de la chance, petit! s'est écrié Grasset. Quel beau déguisement!   Mais si Madame Perle. . . .

—Ne vous inquiétez pas, Monsieur le Commissaire. Ma sœur m'obéit toujours.   N'est-ce pas, Marie?

Mme Perle a fait une moue délicieuse.   Puis elle a soupiré.

—Que veux-tu que . . .?

—Mais rien, mon petit! a interrompu l'inspecteur. Toi et tes enfants, vous allez accompagner ce monsieur à l'aéroport.   Il t'expliquera pourquoi.   En même temps tu vas faire semblant d'être sa femme.

Mme Perle a regardé un moment ses filles.

—Il n'y aura pas de danger?

—Aucun, a promis Grasset.   Vous et l'Inspecteur Lapuce vous tiendrez bras dessus bras dessous à la barrière.   Dès que l'inspecteur aura reconnu ceux qu'il attend, vous pourrez partir.

—Et moi, patron? a demandé Lapuce.

—Tu les suivras.   L'Inspecteur Diamant vous prêtera une voiture. . . .

—Elle est toute prête, Monsieur le Commissaire. La voilà sous ce palmier.   Là-bas . . . une 'Dauphine'* très discrète!   J'y ai mis un émetteur-récepteur,[2] un fusil, deux revolvers et deux grenades lacrymogènes.[3]

—Parfait! a dit Grasset.   Moi, j'attendrai au commissariat.   Tu m'appelleras par émetteur dès que tu auras découvert quelque chose.   Allez-y, mes enfants, et bonne chance.

*   *   *

---

[1] profession   [2] walkie-talkie   [3] tear-gas bombs

Le soleil tropical s'est couché sur la Mer des Antilles. Les montagnes lointaines sont devenues violettes, puis bleues, puis noires. Mais Grasset ne faisait pas attention à la beauté du paysage. Il attendait dans une petite salle du commissariat. Il avait déjà fumé huit pipes.

—Mais qu'est-ce qu'il fait, ce petit? a-t-il grommelé.

Il était seul. L'Inspecteur Diamant était parti chercher sa sœur qui n'était pas revenue.

Soudain la porte s'est ouverte. C'était l'inspecteur. Il était pâle comme la mort.

—On a trouvé la 'Dauphine', cachée dans les ruines de Saint-Pierre.* Ma sœur, les deux enfants, votre inspecteur, ont tous disparu. . . .

NOTES

la D.S.: one of the most successful Citroen models.

Le Marais: means literally '*The Marsh*'. It is an ancient district of Paris famous for its old 'hôtels' (mansions), many of which are now being restored.

Place des Vosges: a magnificent arcaded square built in the 16th century. The great 19th century writer, Victor Hugo, lived there for a while, and his house is now a museum.

Martinique: (see map, page 18) a beautiful island in the West Indies (**Les Antilles**). It was once a French colony, but is now a '**département**' and elects its own representatives to sit in the French Parliament. The population consists of **Créoles** (natives of European stock, mostly French), Negroes (descendants of slaves) and people of mixed blood. The word '**Créole**' is often wrongly used to denote *any* native of the French West Indies.

Fort-de-France: capital and chief port of the island.

L'Impératrice Joséphine: *the Empress Josephine*, first wife of Napoleon, was a Créole. She was born and brought up in Martinique. The ruins of her house, La Pagerie, are a show-place on the island.

La Guadeloupe: another important French island in the Caribbean (**Mer des Antilles**). It lies about 100 miles north of Martinique.

Dauphine: a very popular small Renault car.

Saint-Pierre: See Note at the end of the next chapter.

4 L'EXPLOSION

Grasset et l'Inspecteur Diamant sont partis tout de suite pour Saint-Pierre.* Ils ont pris la Route de la Trace* qui traversait la magnifique forêt tropicale. La route était déserte. La forêt dormait mystérieusement sous les rayons de la pleine lune. Les deux hommes ne parlaient pas.

—Voilà la Montagne Pelée,* a dit enfin l'Inspecteur Diamant. Les ruines de Saint-Pierre se trouvent au pied de la montagne.

Grasset a regardé la silhouette noire de ce volcan sinistre qui avait détruit une ville entière et tué tous ses habitants. Un petit nuage blanc flottait au-dessus du sommet. L'inspecteur semblait deviner les pensées du Commissaire.

—Il est éteint, a-t-il remarqué.

Ils sont arrivés enfin à la ville morte. La 'Dauphine' était gardée par quatre gendarmes. Elle était cachée sous des fougères[1] et des plantes grimpantes.

—Comment l'avez-vous trouvée? a demandé Grasset.

Un des gendarmes a rougi.

—Je n'étais pas de service, Monsieur le Commissaire. Je me promenais ici avec ma fiancée . . . au clair de lune . . . quand soudain j'ai remarqué quelque chose qui brillait. Je me suis dit que ce n'était pas naturel. Alors je suis allé voir, et j'ai vu que c'était le pare-brise[2] d'une voiture . . . celle-ci.

—Est-ce que c'est Lapuce qui l'a conduite ici ou . . . quelqu'un d'autre? Voilà la question, a dit Grasset.

Puis il s'est tourné vers Diamant.

[1] *la fougère*, fern   [2] windscreen

La 'Dauphine' était gardée par quatre gendarmes

—J'ai l'impression que votre sœur est une femme très raisonnable . . . trop raisonnable pour courir des risques, n'est-ce pas?

—Oui, Monsieur le Commissaire, elle aime trop ses enfants pour courir des risques.

—Alors si elle n'est pas revenue c'est parce qu'on l'a empêchée de revenir.

Grasset était sur le point d'ouvrir la portière de la voiture, quand il a entendu le ronron d'un moteur qui semblait venir du côté de la Route de la Trace. Il a reconnu le bruit tout de suite. Tous les hommes se sont tus et ont dirigé leurs regards vers la forêt. Dix secondes plus tard ils ont vu au clair de lune un énorme hélicoptère qui descendait du ciel comme un oiseau préhistorique et disparaissait derrière les arbres.

—C'est curieux! s'est écrié Diamant. L'île n'est pas très grande, mais c'est la première fois que je vois cet appareil.[1] Du reste je me demande où il va atterrir.

—Vous voulez dire qu'il n'y a pas de propriété, pas de terrain plat de ce côté-là? a demandé Grasset.

—Si, il y a une grande maison au beau milieu de la forêt. Elle a un toit en terrasse assez large pour un hélicoptère, mais voici des années* qu'elle est inoccupée.

—Vous avez visité cette maison récemment?

—Non, mais on m'a dit que toutes les portes sont fermées et qu'il est impossible de voir à l'intérieur à cause des grands volets en fer.

—A qui appartient-elle?

—Elle appartient à un Chinois très riche qui est venu de Tahiti il y a vingt-cinq ans. Il a épousé une Française très belle et très riche qui . . .

—Lui a donné une fille, n'est-ce pas? a interrompu Grasset.

[1] machine

—Oui, a répondu Diamant très surpris.   Alors vous connaissez la famille?

—Oui et non! a dit Grasset en faisant la grimace. Mais continuez.

—La mère est morte deux ans après la naissance de sa fille, et le père est parti avec le bébé on ne sait où.

—Alors ma petite Chinoise blonde a peut-être vingt-trois ans, a dit Grasset, sortant son revolver de sa poche et montant dans la voiture de l'inspecteur.   Conduisez-moi tout de suite à cette maison.   Je crois que nous n'arriverons pas à temps, mais . . . j'espère que tous vos hommes sont armés. Allons! Allons! Nous n'avons pas une minute à perdre.

*   *   *

—Je ne trouve pas le chemin, a dit l'inspecteur de plus en plus inquiet.

Ils avaient traversé la forêt en voiture trois fois, avançant très lentement et sans faire de bruit.

—Est-ce qu'elle existe, cette maison? a demandé ironiquement Grasset.   Ce que vous m'avez raconté, ce n'est pas un conte de fées?[1]

—Mais non, Monsieur le Commissaire! a répondu le pauvre inspecteur, qui pensait avec angoisse à sa sœur et à ses deux nièces.

Soudain un des gendarmes a crié, 'Le voici, le chemin, mais impossible de passer.'   Le chemin avait en effet été envahi par la forêt.   Il était couvert de hautes fougères et de plantes grimpantes qui formaient une barrière infranchissable.

—Il faut continuer à pied, a grommelé Grasset.   Je suppose que vous avez apporté des haches. . . .

—Naturellement, Monsieur le Commissaire.

[1] fairy tale

Ils avançaient avec peine à la lumière de deux lampes électriques, frappant à droite et à gauche, s'écorchant les mains et le visage, transpirant abondamment. A chaque pas Grasset s'imaginait que des serpents s'enroulaient autour de son cou. Des milliers de moustiques[1] s'abattaient sur lui, le piquant au nez, aux joues, aux yeux. Jamais il ne s'était senti si malheureux.

Soudain un des gendarmes a soufflé, 'Je crois que nous y sommes. Je vois un bâtiment.'

Grasset a levé ses yeux gonflés[2] et à travers les feuilles énormes d'un bananier il a vu au clair de lune une longue maison blanche. Au même instant le bruit sinistre de l'hélicoptère a rompu le silence. L'inspecteur s'est précipité.

—Doucement! a chuchoté Grasset.

L'inspecteur s'est arrêté, jetant un regard angoissé vers l'hélicoptère qui s'élevait lourdement. Dix secondes après l'énorme appareil avait disparu dans la nuit.

—Nous sommes arrivés trop tard, s'est écrié l'inspecteur au désespoir.

—On va voir, a grommelé Grasset. Allons! Nous. . . .

Une violente explosion lui a coupé la parole et l'a jeté par terre. Quand il s'est relevé il a vu que la maison avait disparu. La force de l'explosion avait tout rasé, à l'exception de la moitié d'un mur. L'inspecteur regardait les ruines fumantes, les yeux pleins de larmes.

—Assassins! a-t-il crié.

Grasset a essayé de le consoler.

—Du courage! Je crois que votre sœur et vos enfants vivent toujours, et mon petit inspecteur aussi. En avant! Mais faites attention. Ils ont peut-être laissé une arrière-garde.

[1] *la moustique*, mosquito   [2] swollen

Ils se sont avancés à pas de loup.[1]   Peu à peu le nuage de fumée et de poussière s'est dissipé.   Ils sont arrivés aux ruines sans incidents.

—Personne! a déclaré Grasset au bout de cinq minutes de recherches.   Pas un cadavre![2]   Même pas un blessé!   Ma petite Chinoise blonde et ses amis les ont emmenés dans l'hélicoptère.   Mais où?   Voilà la question.

Tout à coup l'inspecteur a crié, 'J'ai trouvé une trappe,[3] Monsieur le Commissaire.'

Deux gendarmes ont soulevé la trappe qui était à moitié cachée sous les décombres.[4]   Des marches descendaient dans l'obscurité.

Grasset a souri amèrement.[5]

—C'est parfait!   Une maison que tout le monde croit abandonnée, un passage secret qui mène à Saint-Pierre, une jetée, des canots, un yacht . . . oui, c'est parfait.   Mais cette fois-ci ils ont eu besoin pour leur fuite de quelque chose de plus rapide qu'un yacht. Cela explique l'hélicoptère.

—Mais qu'est-ce qu'on va faire? a demandé le pauvre inspecteur qui pensait toujours à sa sœur.

—On va retourner tout de suite à l'aéroport, a répondu Grasset.   Là je monterai dans ce maudit avion à réaction et je donnerai ordre de partir pour Tahiti.

NOTES

Saint-Pierre: (See map, page 18) the former capital of the island.   In 1902 it was completely wiped out by an eruption of the volcano, **la Montagne Pelée**.   There was only one survivor out of a population of 40,000. There is now a new Saint-Pierre, but some of the ruins remain.

[1] stealthily	[2] corpse	[3] trap-door
[4] rubble	[5] bitterly	

Route de la Trace: a hilly, scenic road through tropical forest.

voici des années qu'elle est inoccupée: *it has been unoccupied for years.*

5   LA CHINOISE BLONDE SE VENGE

Lapuce, Mme Perle et ses deux filles attendaient parmi la foule à la barrière de l'aéroport.   Lapuce tenait par la main une des petites filles qui le regardait de ses grands yeux noirs.   L'avion de Paris venait d'arriver.

—Je cherche un homme qui a le bras droit plus court que le gauche, a expliqué Lapuce . . . et une Chinoise aux cheveux blonds!

A peine les premiers passagers étaient-ils arrivés à la barrière que Lapuce a soufflé, 'La voilà, la petite Chinoise blonde!'

—Pas possible! s'est écriée Mme Perle.   Je la connais.   Nous étions à la même école à la Guadeloupe.   Une petite sorcière . . .!

—Cachez-vous derrière moi, a chuchoté Lapuce d'une voix pressante.   Si elle vous reconnaît. . . .

Mais il était trop tard.   La 'Chinoise blonde' s'est arrêtée et s'est mise à parler à un des hommes qui l'accompagnaient.   L'homme a fait un geste d'impatience, et Lapuce a remarqué en frissonnant que son bras droit était plus court que celui d'un enfant. . . .   La 'Chinoise blonde' a couru vers Mme Perle.

—Mais quelle surprise!   Je te croyais à la Guadeloupe.

—Je suis en vacances, a répondu Mme Perle, se forçant à sourire.

—Et tu es mariée! a continué la 'Chinoise blonde', regardant les petites filles.   Comme elles sont mignonnes!*

Puis elle a regardé Lapuce.

—Et . . . ce monsieur est ton mari?

32

—Oui, a balbutié Mme Perle. Al . . . Alphonse, je vous . . . te* présente Mlle Hari, une ancienne camarade de classe.

—Enchanté, mademoiselle, a dit Lapuce.

—Je suis vraiment ravie de te revoir, Marie, a repris Mlle Hari. Vous avez le temps de venir boire quelque chose? . . . pas ici. Ce serait plus agréable à Fort-de-France, n'est-ce pas? Nous aurons tant de choses à nous raconter.

—Mais . . . mais nous attendons des amis, a répondu Mme Perle en rougissant.

—Eh bien, vos amis ont dû manquer l'avion, a dit Mlle Hari ironiquement. Regarde! Nous sommes les derniers.

—Nous serions enchantés d'accepter votre invitation, mademoiselle, a dit Lapuce. Comme vous l'avez déjà fait observer, nos amis ont certainement manqué l'avion. Si vous voulez bien passer devant. . . .

—Mais non! Je viens avec vous. Vous êtes venus en voiture? Bon! Je me mettrai à l'arrière entre vos charmantes fillettes. Mes amis nous suivront dans la Citroën.

Les deux voitures se sont mises en marche. Lapuce éprouvait quelque inquiétude. L'affaire tournait mal. Est-ce que cette petite 'sorcière' avait deviné que c'était un 'flic'? Que feraient ses trois amis s'ils savaient qu'il appartenait à la Police Judiciaire? Il pouvait les voir dans le rétroviseur[1] de la 'Dauphine'. Ils avaient l'air sinistre, surtout l'homme au bras court. Il se demandait s'ils étaient armés. Soudain le chauffeur de la Citroën a accéléré pour doubler[2] la 'Dauphine', et en même temps Mlle Hari a crié, 'Arrêtez! . . . tout de suite! Je suis armée.'

[1] (car) mirror   [2] to overtake

Lapuce a vu la Citroën disparaître à toute vitesse dans un virage.[1]   La route était déserte.   Il a arrêté la voiture pendant que Mme Perle le regardait épouvantée.

—Vous pouvez au moins laisser partir ma femme et mes enfants. . . .

—Votre femme! a sifflé la 'Chinoise blonde'.   Je ne sais pas qui vous êtes, monsieur, mais vous n'êtes certainement pas le mari de Marie.   Vous n'êtes même pas marié.   Vous ne portez pas d'alliance.*   Dans mon métier on ne court pas de risques. . . . N'ayez pas peur, mes petits, a-t-elle dit aux fillettes qui s'étaient mises à pleurer.   On ne vous fera pas de mal. . . . Toi, Marie, pourquoi as-tu menti?   Qu'est-ce que tu mijotes,[2] hein?   Tu. . . .

Lapuce s'est retourné brusquement et a vu que la 'Chinoise blonde' portait un masque à gaz.   Au même instant il a perdu connaissance. . . .

*   *   *

—Iaora, monsieur!   Cela veut dire dans la langue de ces îles, 'Vous êtes le bienvenu'.   Vous avez bien dormi, j'espère?

En ouvrant les yeux Lapuce s'est trouvé face à face avec un gros Chinois d'un certain âge, qui ne portait rien qu'un caleçon de bain[3] et un chapeau de feuilles. Le Chinois s'est tu pendant que Lapuce regardait autour de lui.   Il était étendu sur un lit de fougères dans une chambre sans meubles.   Les murs étaient faits de bambou et le toit de chaume.[4]   Mais ce qui l'a

---

[1] bend   [2] what are you up to?   [3] bathing slip   [4] thatch

—*Iaora, monsieur!*

frappé tout de suite, c'est la vue qui s'offrait* à ses yeux.

La chambre donnait sur une lagune encore plus bleue que le ciel sans nuages.   La plage de sable blanc était bordée d'une forêt de hauts palmiers qui s'étendait à perte de vue.   Il entendait le bruit d'une cascade et voyait un torrent qui bouillonnait entre des rochers couverts de fougères et de fleurs exotiques.   Au-dessus des palmiers il entrevoyait les pics dentelés[1] d'une chaîne de montagnes.   Jamais il n'avait rien vu de si beau.

—Iaora! a répété son hôte, se levant et lui mettant autour du cou une guirlande* de fleurs écarlates. Vous vous croyez toujours à la Martinique, n'est-ce pas?   Eh bien, vous êtes loin des Antilles, mon ami, très, très loin.   Vous avez entendu parler de la Polynésie,*   de Bora-Bora,   de Tahiti?... Vous admirez la vue!   Elle est ravissante, n'est-ce pas, le paradis terrestre.[2]   Eh bien, ce paradis est à vous, mon ami, parce que ... vous allez y passer le reste de votre vie. ...

Lapuce s'est frotté les yeux.   Est-ce qu'il rêvait? Ce gros Chinois presque nu qui le regardait si doucement, est-ce que c'était le chef de cette sinistre Organisation Fantôme?   Est-ce que c'était le père de la petite 'Chinoise blonde'?

—Mon associé américain, a repris le Chinois. ... Oui, vous le connaissez déjà.   C'est celui qui a le bras droit plus court que le gauche.   Un accident, vous comprenez.   Dans notre métier on court des risques. ... Eh bien, mon associé demande votre mort.   Mais moi, Ho Ming, je suis un homme pacifique.   Oui, monsieur, je ne suis pas un assassin.   Je suis un homme

---

[1] jagged   [2] paradise on earth

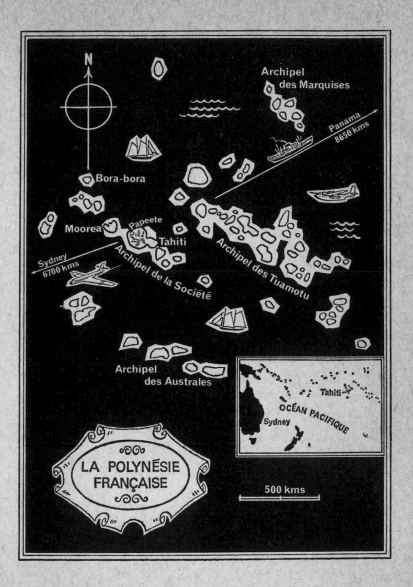

N

Archipel
des Marquises

Panama
8650 kms

Bora-bora

Moorea   Papeete
          Tahiti

Sydney
6700 kms   Archipel de la Société   Archipel des Tuamotu

Archipel
des Australes

Tahiti
OCÉAN PACIFIQUE
Sydney

LA POLYNÉSIE
FRANÇAISE

500 kms

d'affaires. . . . Ah! vous voudriez savoir *quelles* affaires, n'est-ce pas? Je vous dirai tout un de ces jours, mais . . . pour le moment parlons de vous, monsieur. Je ne vous demanderai pas qui vous êtes. Je ne saurais pas si vous mentiez. En tout cas nous sommes déjà en train de nous renseigner sur vous. . . . J'ai des agents partout dans le monde, vous comprenez, monsieur. . . . Si vous êtes innocent, vous vivrez. Sinon . . . si, par exemple, vous êtes un espion, ou si vous appartenez à la police. . . .

Le Chinois s'est tu. Il ne souriait plus. Lapuce a essayé de se lever, mais il était trop faible.

—Et la . . . a-t-il commencé.

—Ah! Vous allez me demander des nouvelles de votre 'femme' et de vos 'enfants'! Ne vous inquiétez pas. Elles vont bien. Ce gaz 'lacrymogène' est tout à fait inoffensif . . . un long sommeil, c'est tout. Comme je vous l'ai déjà dit, je suis un homme pacifique. . . .

Puis sans un mot de plus il s'est levé brusquement et a quitté la chambre.

Pendant les quinze jours qui ont suivi Lapuce n'a pas revu Ho Ming. Mais il a mené une vie très agréable. Le matin il se baignait dans la lagune. L'après-midi il dormait sur le sable à l'ombre des palmiers. Il faisait d'excellents repas. Jamais il n'avait goûté de poisson plus savoureux ni de fruits plus succulents.

Mais on ne le laissait jamais seul. Trois pêcheurs polynésiens, armés de long couteaux, ne le lâchaient pas d'une semelle.[1] C'étaient des hommes joviaux qui riaient tout le temps. Lapuce les trouvait très sympathiques. Ils lui apprenaient à pêcher, à tuer des

---

[1] The nearest equivalent in English is 'stuck to him like limpets'.
Literally it means 'did not let him go by a sole of a foot'.

requins[1], à grimper aux hauts palmiers. 'Un de ces jours, se disait-il, ces gaillards vont m'aider à m'évader.'

Un soir qu'il était assis à regarder le grand soleil rouge descendre à l'horizon, Ho Ming a reparu soudain devant lui.

—Bonsoir, Monsieur *Lapuce*, a-t-il dit d'une voix triste. Je regrette. . . . Ah! Je vois que vous avez deviné pourquoi je suis venu. . . .

Lapuce s'était levé. Les deux hommes se regardaient droit dans les yeux.

—Mais il y a moyen d'avoir la vie sauve,* mon ami, a continué Ho Ming. Nous savons que vous avez été accompagné à la Martinique par le Commissaire Grasset. Nous savons que c'est lui qui a volé la formule à ma fille. C'est un homme très habile que le Commissaire Grasset! Il a sans doute recueilli des renseignements très intéressantes sur l'Organisation Fantôme. Nous voudrions savoir. . . .

—Vous ne lui avez pas téléphoné au Quai des Orfèvres? a ironisé Lapuce.

—Ah! Vous aimez plaisanter, Monsieur Lapuce. C'est bien! Je m'en vais. Mais j'espère que vous serez plus raisonnable quand je reviendrai, sans quoi . . . je vous jetterai aux requins! A tout à l'heure, Monsieur Lapuce.

Lapuce a regardé le vaste océan qui s'étendait au delà du récif.[2] Que cachait-elle, cette mer si bleue, si calme? Les requins! Il a frissonné. Puis il s'est tourné vers ses trois gardiens qui s'approchaient de lui. Mais ils ne riaient plus. Ils ont empoigné leurs couteaux luisants comme s'ils voulaient les lui plonger dans le corps. Au même instant il a entendu le bruit d'un hydravion.

[1] *le requin*, shark   [2] reef

NOTES

Comme elles sont mignonnes!: *How sweet they are!*

Je vous . . . te présente: as the 'wife' of Lapuce, Mme Perle would address him as '**tu**'—not '**vous**'.

alliance (*f.*): *wedding ring.* It is very unusual today to see a married Frenchman without a wedding ring.

la vue qui s'offrait à ses yeux: *the view which met his eyes.*

La Polynésie: *Polynesia,* the name given to the numerous archipelagos (groups of islands) which dot the South East Pacific. **Bora-Bora** and **Tahiti** are two of the 130 coral islands of French Polynesia—an area as vast as Europe. Tahiti, the most famous of all Polynesian islands, lies halfway between the U.S.A. and Australia and is an important port of call both for ships and airliners. Its beauty and the beauty of its people, were made famous by the 19th century French painter, Gauguin. French, Polynesians and Chinese live happily together on the island and there has been much inter-marrying. The population of the island is 45,000, of whom 18,000 live in the little unspoiled capital, Papeete.

guirlandes (*f.*): *garlands.* Polynesians greet visitors to their islands by putting garlands of flowers round their necks.

il y a moyen d'avoir la vie sauve: *there is a way of saving your life.*

6   L'ÎLE DES MYSTÈRES

Pour la première fois de sa vie le Commissaire Grasset
a consenti à se déguiser.   Deux heures après son départ
du Lamentin il avait donné ordre au pilote de changer
de route . . . destination Sydney!   A Sydney il s'est
fait jaunir* la peau et a mis une barbe postiche.[1]   Puis
deux jours plus tard il a pris le vol régulier à destination
de Tahiti.

Le dix juin l'avion a atterri sur la magnifique piste de
Tahiti.   Un taxi attendait Grasset à l'aéroport et l'a
conduit tout de suite au commissariat de Papeete.*
Il se sentait mal à l'aise sous son déguisement et ne
songeait pas à admirer la charmante petite capitale,
avec ses fleurs, ses beaux magasins et ses jolies femmes.
Il ne pensait qu'à Mme Perle et ses enfants, au petit
Lapuce et surtout à la 'Chinoise blonde', la fille du chef
de la sinistre Organisation Fantôme.   Que pouvait
bien mijoter ce petit monstre à l'air si innocent?

Il savait maintenant que l'Organisation Fantôme se
composait d'espions internationaux qui volaient des
secrets militaires à toutes les puissances atomiques, aux
Américains, aux Russes, aux Anglais, aux Français et
aux Chinois.   La formule qu'il avait trouvée dans la
montre de la 'Chinoise blonde', par exemple, concern-
ait la partie la plus essentielle d'une nouvelle fusée
britannique.   Les 'fantômes' revendaient les secrets au
plus offrant.[2] . . .

—Des espions à Tahiti! s'est écrié le Commissaire
Paopoa.   Impossible!   Il y a des centaines de Chinois

[1] artificial   [2] highest bidder

4   41

sur l'île.   Ce sont tous des gens très respectables.   Mais je vous aiderai de mon mieux.

Grasset a passé huit jours à explorer l'île. Il a interrogé . . . très discrètement . . . tous les Chinois. Il a visité toutes les plages, toutes les lagunes, tous les cafés dans l'espoir de revoir sa petite 'Chinoise blonde'. Il a loué un cheval et a cherché dans toutes les vallées de l'intérieur. Il a survolé toutes les montagnes, parce qu'il se disait qu'il y avait peut-être quelque maison secrète cachée sous la végétation tropicale, ou dans un creux[1] parmi les montagnes. Il n'a rien trouvé.

—Il reste les autres îles des archipels, a proposé le Commissaire Paopoa, à la fin de la semaine.

—Combien y en a-t-il?

—Mon Dieu! il y en a plus de cent.

—Tant mieux! Prêtez-moi un hydravion.* Je partirai demain.

Un pressentiment lui disait qu'il allait trouver ce qu'il cherchait sur un des innombrables atolls.[2] Il en a visité des douzaines. Les habitants lui offraient des noix de coco et des bananes, mais ils ne l'aidaient pas à éclaircir le mystère. Au bout de la deuxième semaine il n'avait toujours rien découvert. Il est allé voir le Commissaire Paopoa.

—Ce Chinois millionnaire dont vous m'avez parlé l'autre jour, celui qui habitait autrefois ce que vous appelez 'l'île des mystères', vous êtes absolument sûr qu'il est mort?

—Mais oui, a répondu Paopoa. J'ai assisté à son enterrement . . . il y a six ans.

—Et sa maison . . . ?

—Elle a été démolie.   C'était un homme bizarre.

---

[1] hole, hollow   [2] coral island

Il a légué sa propriété à des pêcheurs polynésiens qui sont maintenant les seuls habitants de l'île. . . .

—Un enterrement! s'est écrié Grasset. Ça, c'est le coup classique![1] Mon petit doigt* me dit que votre Chinois millionnaire vit toujours. En tout cas j'ai l'intention de visiter cette 'île des mystères' . . . en compagnie de dix hommes armés . . . si vous les avez.

A sept heures du soir l'hydravion approchait de l'île. Dix minutes plus tard, pendant que l'avion rasait les sommets des montagnes, Grasset s'est écrié soudain:

—Regardez! Cette antenne[2] là-bas! Vous ne l'avez pas remarquée? Il y a une antenne . . . mais pas de bâtiment!

L'hydravion est descendu sur la lagune. Grasset, Paopoa et dix gendarmes armés de mitraillettes[3] ont sauté dans des canots. A sept heures vingt ils ont pris pied sur le sable blanc de 'l'île des mystères'.

Sur la plage il y avait deux bateaux de pêche et au loin, cachée sous des palmiers au bord d'un torrent, une petite hutte. Ils sont entrés dans la hutte. Il n'y avait personne, mais Grasset a tout de suite remarqué une paire de chaussures.

—Ce ne sont pas des chaussures de pêcheurs! Allons! Nous n'avons pas une minute à perdre. Il faut trouver cette antenne.

Ils ont suivi le torrent. La vallée, qui devenait de plus en plus profonde, était semée de rochers. La végétation était si abondante qu'ils avaient de la peine à avancer. Mais tout à coup Grasset, qui marchait le premier, a crié:

—Arrêtez!

Ils étaient arrivés à une clairière.[4] Devant eux se

[1] an old trick
[2] wireless aerial
[3] *la mitraillette*, tommy-gun
[4] clearing

dressait un grand rocher à moitié caché par un nuage blanc.

—De la fumée, a affirmé Paopoa.

—Non, a repliqué Grasset, du gaz!

En même temps quatre hommes, portant des masques à gaz et armés de mitraillettes, se sont précipités vers eux. Grasset était sur le point de hurler, 'Feu!' quand. . . .

* * *

Lorsque Lapuce a entendu le bruit de l'hydravion il a essayé une ruse audacieuse. Se tournant vers ses trois gardiens il a montré du doigt l'hydravion qu'ils pouvaient tous voir maintenant.

—C'est la police. Si vous m'aidez, on sera indulgent[1] envers vous.

A sa grande surprise ils ont tout de suite jeté leurs couteaux et sont venus lui serrer la main. Il les a regardés avec curiosité, se demandant s'il pouvait se fier[2] à eux. Enfin il s'est décidé.

—Parfait! Eh bien, menez-moi chez votre chef.

—C'est impossible, a répondu l'un d'eux. Personne ne sait où il demeure.

—Et la femme et les deux fillettes? Où se trouvent-elles?

L'homme s'est tu.

—Elles sont mortes? a demandé Lapuce épouvanté.

—Pas encore, mais si la fille du chef. . . .

—Moi, je sais où demeure le chef, a dit soudain un autre. Je l'ai découvert il y a quelques mois, mais je n'ai osé le dire à personne.

Lapuce a regardé l'homme droit dans les yeux.

[1] lenient   [2] *se fier à*, to trust

—Vous ne mentez pas?

—Non.

—Bon! Montrez-nous le chemin.

L'homme les a menés à un petit sentier tortueux qui
creusait un chemin à travers la forêt. Le sentier
montait vers les montagnes longeant la rive droite du
torrent. De temps en temps Lapuce entrevoyait les
pics bleus à travers les feuilles. Leur guide s'arrêtait
assez souvent pour regarder autour de lui. Il semblait
avoir peur. Mais enfin il a murmuré:

—Nous approchons. A vingt pas d'ici il y a un
tunnel. Je ne m'y suis jamais aventuré, mais j'en ai
vu l'entrée. Elle est cachée sous des plantes grimpantes. Il y aura certainement une sentinelle . . .
peut-être plusieurs aujourd'hui à cause de l'hydravion.
Que faut-il faire?

Lapuce n'a pas hésité.

—En avant! Nous allons leur faire une surprise.

—La voilà, la sentinelle! a soudain chuchoté le guide.
Il n'y en a qu'une seule.

A dix pas de l'endroit où ils se trouvaient un homme
à demi-nu était assis devant un rideau de fleurs
écarlates. Il était armé d'une mitraillette et toutes les
dix secondes il regardait à droite et à gauche. Mais le
bruit du torrent l'empêchait d'entendre tout autre bruit.
Alors Lapuce et ses trois compagnons ont pu s'approcher
sans être remarqués. Un des Polynésiens avait tiré
son couteau.

—On va lui couper la gorge! a-t-il proposé.

—Non! a dit Lapuce. Laissez-moi faire.

Il s'est précipité sur la sentinelle, l'a jetée à terre, lui
a lié[1] les mains avec sa ceinture[2] et l'a bâillonnée[3] avec
son mouchoir. Puis il a écarté le rideau de fleurs et,

---

[1] *lier*, to bind   [2] *belt*   [3] *bâillonner*, to gag

suivi des trois Polynésiens, il est entré dans la forteresse de l'Organisation Fantôme.

Ils se trouvaient dans un long couloir qui pénétrait dans le flanc de la montagne.   A droite et à gauche il y avait des portes, d'où venait un bruit de voix.   Lapuce s'est approché d'une des portes.   Une voix à l'accent américain criait en mauvais français, 'Vous auriez dû* le tuer sur-le-champ.'   Puis une autre voix douce, que Lapuce a reconnue tout de suite pour celle de Ho Ming, a répondu, 'Nous n'avons rien à craindre.   Cet hydravion amène des touristes, j'en suis sûr. J'ai donné ordre de cacher les prisonniers.'   'Tu es fou, papa,' a crié une voix de femme.   'Il faut le tuer. C'est un flic.   Je déteste les flics!'

Soudain Lapuce a remarqué qu'une des portes était entr'ouverte.   Après avoir écouté un instant il l'a poussée et a vu, entassés sur des rayons, des masques à gaz, des grenades lacrymogènes et des mitraillettes.

—Attrapez! a-t-il soufflé à ses compagnons, leur jetant à chacun un masque et une mitraillette.

Puis mettant lui-même un masque, il a pris une grenade et, se précipitant dans le couloir, il a crié d'une voix forte:

—Bonsoir, messieurs-dames!

Il y a eu un silence.   Puis tout d'un coup, toutes les portes se sont ouvertes.   Il a jeté la grenade . . .

* * *

Ils étaient tous sur la plage de 'l'île des mystères'. Grasset a regardé Lapuce en souriant.

—Bravo, petit!   Je crois que nous avons attrapé toute la bande, y compris ma petite Chinoise blonde. Regarde le joli petit monstre!   Elle dort comme un bébé!   Tu es sûr que ce gaz est inoffensif?

—*Que je suis content de vous revoir! s'est écrié Lapuce*

Tous les 'fantômes' . . . il y en avait cinquante-cinq . . . étaient étendus sur le sable au bord de la lagune. On attendait un deuxième hydravion. Bientôt deux gendarmes sont arrivés avec Mme Perle et ses enfants. On les avait trouvées enfermées dans une goélette ancrée dans une lagune de l'autre côté de l'île. Mme Perle tenait à la main un gros bouquet de fleurs tropicales et les fillettes portaient deux énormes noix de coco. Elles semblaient très heureuses.

—Que je suis content* de vous revoir! s'est écrié Lapuce en les embrassant toutes les trois sur les deux joues.

Quelques minutes plus tard d'autres policiers ont amené le diplomate français qui avait été kidnappé à Londres.

—Je vois que vous n'êtes pas mort, s'est écrié Grasset étonné.

—Loin de là! Je viens de passer les jours les plus heureux de ma vie.

—Moi aussi, a murmuré Lapuce.

—Tais-toi, petit! a grommelé Grasset en regardant les cinquante-cinq 'fantômes' qui dormaient tranquillement sur le sable.

Le soleil se couchait. Un vent léger agitait les cimes des palmiers et ridait la surface bleue de la lagune.

—C'est beau, a-t-il murmuré, mais quand même j'aime mieux les platanes[1] des boulevards et l'eau sale de la Seine.

NOTES

il s'est fait jaunir la peau: *he had his skin stained yellow.*
Vous auriez dû le tuer: *You ought to have killed him.*

[1] *le platane,* plane-tree

un hydravion: *sea-plane.* Some of the islands are linked by sea-plane, but a more delightful way of visiting them all is by schooner (**goélette**).

mon petit doigt me dit: *a little bird tells me* (**doigt,** finger).

Que je suis content de vous revoir!: *How pleased I am to see you!*

QUESTIONNAIRE

——— ✱ ———

I—LA CHINOISE BLONDE

1. Qu'y avait-il dans les sacs des jeunes Anglaises?
2. Pourquoi le Commissaire Grasset était-il allé à Londres?
3. Faites la description de la jeune fille qui regardait Grasset.
4. Comment Grasset a-t-il retourné le compliment à la 'Chinoise blonde'?
5. Qu'est-ce qui était curieux?
6. Comment Grasset a-t-il encouragé la 'Chinoise blonde'?
7. Qu'est-ce qui montre que la 'Chinoise blonde' était Française?
8. Est-ce que le douanier a été gentil avec elle?
9. Pourquoi lui a-t-il pris la main gauche?
10. Pourquoi la femme en uniforme a-t-elle emmené la 'Chinoise blonde'?

*　　*　　*

11. Pourquoi Grasset n'est-il pas redescendu sur le quai?
12. Pourquoi la 'Chinoise blonde' est-elle montée aussitôt dans le train?
13. Qui était dans le compartiment avec Grasset?
14. Pourquoi la Suissesse a-t-elle rougi?
15. Quelle pensée a fait sourire Grasset?
16. Pourquoi les Anglais ont-ils regardé sévèrement Grasset?
17. Comment sait-on que Grasset mentait?
18. Pourquoi la 'Chinoise blonde' a-t-elle tourné le dos au contrôleur?
19. Combien de pipes avait-il déjà fumées?
20. Avez-vous jamais passé quelque chose en contrebande?

II—LA CHAMBRE DES ESPIONS

1. Pourquoi Grasset a-t-il fait semblant de ne pas re-marquer la 'Chinoise blonde' et ses deux compagnons?
2. Pourquoi était-il certain qu'on allait le suivre?
3. Où était l'hôtel?
4. Pourquoi le patron appelait-il sa meilleure chambre 'la chambre des espions'?
5. Où était-elle située?
6. Pourquoi Grasset s'est-il assis sur le lit?
7. Pourquoi la montre était-elle si légère?
8. Qui est Lapuce?
9. Quels ordres Grasset a-t-il donnés à Lapuce?
10. Pourquoi le patron a-t-il téléphoné à Grasset?

* * *

11. Qu'a fait Grasset après avoir mis le rouleau dans son portefeuille?
12. Quel risque courait-il?
13. Pourquoi avait-il renoncé à l'idée de se cacher dans l'armoire?
14. A quelle heure a-t-il entendu le bruit?
15. Est-ce que vous ronflez?
16. Pourquoi l'étranger a-t-il poussé un soupir de soulage-ment?
17. Où était Lapuce? Que faisait-il?
18. Pourquoi ce 'quelqu'un' a-t-il téléphoné à Scotland Yard?
19. Pourquoi la formule était-elle si importante à l'avis du chef?
20. Pourquoi Grasset voulait-il aller voir Lapuce?

III—LAPUCE 'SE MARIE'

1. Comment l'homme a-t-il pu entrer à l'hôtel?
2. Où était la voiture de Lapuce?

3. Pourquoi Lapuce a-t-il dit qu'il était difficile de suivre l'homme?

4. Comment Lapuce a-t-il deviné dans quelle maison l'homme était entré?

5. Qu'a fait Lapuce?

6. Pourquoi le père de la femme blâmerait-il (*See Note*, *p.* 14) l'homme à l'accent américain?

7. Comment s'appelle 'le gros Papa'?

8. Lapuce a découvert quelque chose de très important. Quoi?

9. Pourquoi n'était-il plus nécessaire de trouver le traître?

10. Pourquoi Grasset a-t-il décidé de partir tout de suite pour les Antilles?

*   *   *

11. Comment l'Inspecteur Diamant savait-il que Grasset allait arriver?

12. Où ont-ils bu le rhum?

13. Pourquoi l'Inspecteur Diamant était-il si fier du rhum?

14. Pourquoi Grasset ne voulait-il pas se déguiser?

15. Faites la description de Mme Perle.

16. D'où venait-elle?

17. Pourquoi a-t-elle fait une moue?

18. Pourquoi Lapuce aurait-il (*see Note*, *p.* 14) besoin d'une voiture?

19. Qu'est-ce l'Inspecteur Diamant avait mis dans la voiture?

20. Pourquoi Grasset ne faisait-il pas attention à la beauté du paysage?

IV—L'EXPLOSION

1. Pourquoi Grasset et Diamant sont-ils partis tout de suite pour Saint-Pierre?

2. Qu'est-ce qui a détruit Saint-Pierre?

3. Pourquoi le gendarme a-t-il rougi?

4. Comment a-t-il trouvé la Dauphine?
5. Êtes-vous toujours raisonnable?
6. D'où venait l'hélicoptère et où allait-il?
7. Pourquoi Diamant s'est-il écrié, 'C'est curieux!' quand il a vu l'hélicoptère?
8. Où allait atterrir l'hélicoptère à votre avis?
9. Pourquoi était-il impossible d'entrer dans la maison?
10. Qu'a fait le père après la mort de sa femme?

* * *

11. Pourquoi l'inspecteur était-il si inquiet?
12. Qu'est-ce qui avait envahi le chemin?
13. Pourquoi Grasset se sentait-il si malheureux?
14. Où était-il quand il a vu la maison?
15. Pourquoi l'inspecteur était-il au désespoir?
16. Qu'est-ce qui restait de la maison après l'explosion?
17. Pourquoi Grasset a-t-il crié, 'Attention!'?
18. Qu'est-ce qu'ils ont trouvé parmi les ruines?
19. Qu'est-ce qui explique l'hélicoptère?
20. Qu'est-ce que Grasset allait faire en arrivant à l'aéroport?

V—LA CHINOISE BLONDE SE VENGE

1. De quelle couleur sont vos yeux?
2. Pourquoi Lapuce attendait-il l'avion de Paris?
3. Pourquoi la 'Chinoise blonde' s'est-elle arrêtée?
4. Comment s'appelle la 'Chinoise blonde'?
5. Qu'est-ce qu'une camarade de classe?
6. Qu'est-ce que Mlle Hari a fait observer?
7. Où étaient ses trois amis?
8. Pourquoi Mme Perle était-elle épouvantée?
9. Comment Mlle Hari savait-elle que Lapuce n'était pas marié?
10. Pourquoi les petites filles pleuraient-elles?

* * *

11. Votre père est-il jeune, vieux ou d'un certain âge?
    Quel âge a-t-il?
12. Faites la description de la vue qui s'offrait aux yeux de
    Lapuce?
13. Avez-vous entendu parler de Tahiti et de Bora-Bora?
14. Qui est l'associé du Chinois?
15. Pourquoi n'a-t-il pas demandé à Lapuce qui il était?
16. Est-ce que les nouvelles de Mme Perle et de ses enfants
    étaient bonnes?
17. Comment Lapuce a-t-il passé son temps?
18. Qu'est-ce qu'il a appris à faire?
19. Que voulait savoir Ho Ming?
20. Pourquoi Lapuce a-t-il frissonné en regardant la mer?

VI—L'ÎLE DES MYSTÈRES

1. Pourquoi Grasset a-t-il décidé d'aller à Sydney?
2. A qui pensait-il tout le temps?
3. Nommez les puissances atomiques.
4. Pourquoi Grasset a-t-il loué un cheval?
5. Combien de temps a-t-il passé à explorer les atolls?
6. Pourquoi Paopoa était-il persuadé que le Chinois était
   mort?
7. Qu'est-ce que Grasset a décidé de faire?
8. A qui appartenaient les chaussures à votre avis?
9. Pourquoi Grasset a-t-il crié, 'Arrêtez!'?
10. Est-ce que Grasset a hurlé, 'Feu!'?

*   *   *

11. Quelle ruse Lapuce a-t-il essayée?
12. Qui savait où demeurait le chef de l'Organisation
    Fantôme?
13. Combien de sentinelles y avait-il?
14. Pourquoi Lapuce et ses compagnons ont-ils pu
    s'approcher sans être remarqués?

15. Faites la description de la fortresse de l'Organisation Fantôme.
16. Qui aurait dû tuer (*See Note*, *p.* 48) qui?
17. Qu'est-ce que Lapuce a jeté à ses compagnons?
18. Pourquoi attendait-on un deuxième hydravion?
19. Où a-t-on trouvé Mme Perle et ses enfants?
20. Pourquoi Grasset a-t-il grommelé, 'tais-toi, petit!'?

VOCABULARY

———— ✶ ————

Abbreviations: *m.* masculine; *f.* feminine; *pl.* plural; *inf.* infinitive; *pres.* present tense; *imp.* imperfect; *p.p.* past participle; *fut.* future; *cond.* conditional.

ALL IRREGULAR VERBS—even verbs which are *slightly* irregular—have been marked by an asterisk.

N.B. A FEW VERY ELEMENTARY WORDS, and words whose meaning should be obvious, have been omitted.

s'abattre sur, to swoop upon
abondamment, copiously, freely
abondant, abundant, thick
absolument, absolutely
accélérer, to accelerate
à l'accent américain, with an American accent
accompagner, to accompany
acheter, to buy
un **aéroport,** airport
une **affaire,** affair, business; **homme d'affaires,** businessman
affirmer, to declare
un **âge,** age; **d'un certain âge,** middle-aged
un **agent,** agent; policeman
s'agir de, to be a question of
agiter, to shake
agréable, pleasant
aider, to help
aimer, to like; to love
un **air,** appearance, look; air; **avoir l'air (de),** to look like; **Air France,** French Airlines; **à l'air innocent,** innocent-looking

aise: mal à l'aise, uncomfortable
ajouter, to add
aller, to go; **s'en aller,** to go off, leave; **aller bien,** to be well; **vous allez voir,** you'll see; **allons!** come on! **allez-y!** off you go!
allumer, to light
alors, then; so
en **amande,** almond-shaped
amener, to bring
un **ami,** une **amie,** friend
un **an,** year; **elle a 23 ans,** she is 23
ancien, -ienne, old
ancré, anchored
l'anglais (*m.*), English (language)
anglais, English
une **Anglaise,** English woman
l'angoisse (*f.*), anguish
angoissé, anguished
une **année,** year
annoncer, to announce
une **antenne,** wireless aerial
Les Antilles (*f.*), West Indies; **la Mer des Antilles,** Caribbean Sea

56

un **appareil,** machine

un **appartement,** apartment, flat

*appartenir (*pres.* **il appar-tient**), to belong

*appeler, to call; **je m'ap-pelle,** my name is

apporter, to bring

*apprendre (*imp.* **il appre-nait**), to learn; to teach

l'**approche** (*f.*), approach

approcher de, to approach, draw near

s'**approcher de,** to approach, go up to

après, after, afterwards; **le moment d'après,** the moment afterwards

l'**après-midi** (*m.*), (in the) afternoon

un **archipel,** archipelago

une **arme,** weapon

armé (de), armed (with)

l'**Armée** (*f.*) **de l'Air,** Air Force

une **armoire,** wardrobe

(s')**arrêter,** to stop

à l'**arrière,** in the back

une **arrière-garde,** rear-guard

arriver, to arrive; to happen

un **assassin,** murderer

assassiner, to murder

*s'asseoir, to sit down

s'**asseyant,** sitting down

assez, enough; fairly

assis, sitting, seated (*p.p of* **asseoir**)

assister à, to be present at

un **associé,** partner

s'**assurer,** to make sure

attraper, to catch

attendre, to wait (for)

attention: faire attention, to pay attention; to take care; **attention!** be care-ful!

atterrir, to land

aucun, (not) any; no; none

audacieux, -euse, daring

au-dessus, above

aujourd'hui, today; **nous sommes aujourd'hui jeudi,** it's Thursday today

il **aura, nous aurons** (*fut. of* **avoir**)

j'**aurais** (*cond. of* **avoir**) (*see Note, p.* 14)

aussi, also; as, so

aussitôt, immediately

autour de, around

autre, other; **quelqu'un d'autre,** someone else

autrefois, formerly

*s'avancer, to advance

avant, before; **en avant,** forward

s'**aventurer,** to venture

avertir, to warn

un **avion,** aeroplane

un **avis,** opinion; **à votre avis,** in your opinion

*avoir, to have

ayez (*imperative of* **avoir**): **n'ayez pas peur,** don't be afraid

les **bagages** (*m.*), luggage

se **baigner,** to bathe

se **baisser,** to stoop

balbutier, to stammer

le **balcon,** balcony

le **bambou,** bamboo

la **banane,** banana

le **bananier,** banana-tree

la **bande,** gang

la **barbe,** beard

la **barrière,** barrier

bas, basse, low; **à bas du lit,** out of bed

le **bateau,** boat

le **bâtiment,** building

le **bâton de rouge,** lipstick

5

bavarder, to gossip
le **bébé,** baby
le **besoin,** need; **avoir besoin de,** to need
bête, stupid
bien, well; very; **eh bien,** well; **c'est bien,** all right
bien que, although
bientôt, soon; **à bientôt!** see you soon!
le **bienvenu,** welcome
le **bifteck,** beefsteak
le **billet,** ticket
bizarre, strange, peculiar
blâmer, to blame
blanc, white
le **blessé,** wounded person
bleu, blue
blond, fair (-haired), blond
*__boire,** to drink
le **boîtier,** watch-case
bonsoir, good evening
le **bord,** edge; **au bord de,** beside; **au bord de la mer,** at the seaside
bordé, bordered
la **boucle d'oreille,** ear-ring
*__bouger,** to move
bouillonner, to boil
le **bouquet,** bunch
bourrer, to stuff, fill
le **bout,** end
le **bras,** arm; **au bras court,** with the short arm
bref, brief
briller, to shine
britannique, British
le **bruit,** noise
brusquement, suddenly
le **bureau,** office; desk

ça (short for **cela**), that; **c'est ça,** that's right
(se)**cacher,** to hide
camarade (*m. and f.*) **de classe,** school-friend

le **canif,** penknife
le **canot,** dinghy
car, for
la **carte,** card; **carte d'identité,** identity card
cas: en tout cas, in any case
la **cascade,** waterfall
à **cause de,** because of
ce, this; it
ce qui, ce que, which, what
c'est, ce sont, it is, it was
célèbre, famous
celle (*f. of* **celui**), that, the one; **celle-ci,** that one
celui, this, the one; **celui-ci,** this one; the latter; **celui-là,** that one; the former
une **centaine,** about a hundred
cesse: sans cesse, incessantly, without stopping
cesser, to stop, cease
ceux, those
chacun, each (one)
la **chaîne,** chain; range
la **chambre,** room
la **chance,** luck
chanter, to sing
le **chapeau,** hat
chaque, each
charmant, charming
chaud, warm; **faire chaud,** to be warm (weather)
le **chauffeur,** driver
la **chaussure,** shoe
le **chef,** chief, boss
le **chemin,** road, path, way
cher, chère, dear
chercher, to look for
le **cheval** (*pl.* **-aux**), horse
les **cheveux** (*m.*), hair; **aux cheveux blonds,** fair-haired
chez, at, to the house of
le **chiffre,** figure, number
le **Chinois,** Chinese (man)
la **Chinoise,** Chinese woman

la chose, thing
chuchoter, to whisper
le ciel, sky
la cime, top
la Citroën, make of French car
au clair de lune, in the moon-
    light
le client, customer, (hotel)
    guest
le coin, corner
combien, how much, how
    many
comme, as; like; how
le commencement, beginning
*commencer, to begin
comment, how; what
*commettre, to commit
le commissaire, superintend-
    ant of police
le commissariat, police-sta-
    tion
en compagnie de, in the com-
    pany of
le compagnon, companion
le compartiment, compart-
    ment
se composer de, to be com-
    posed of
*comprendre, to understand
compris (p.p. of compren-
    dre); y compris, includ-
    ing
*conduire (pres. vous con-
    duisez, p.p. conduit), to
    lead; to drive
je connais, il connaît (pres. of
    connaître)
la connaissance: perdre con-
    naissance, to lose con-
    sciousness
*connaître (imp. il connais-
    sait), to know
*consentir (à), to consent,
    agree to
consoler, to comfort
au contraire, on the contrary

contre, against
le contrebandier, smuggler
le contrôleur, ticket collector
le côté, side; à côté de, beside;
    de l'autre côté, on the
    other side; à côté, along-
    side
le cou, neck
se coucher, to go to bed; to set
    (of sun)
le couloir, corridor
le coup, blow; tout à coup,
    suddenly; tout d'un coup,
    all of a sudden
couper, to cut (see parole)
*courir (p.p. couru), to run
court, short
le couteau (pl. -eaux), knife
couvert (de), covered (with)
*craindre, to fear
creuser un chemin, to cut a
    way (through)
crier, to cry, shout
*croire (pres. je crois, nous
    croyons), to believe, think
se croiser, to cross; to meet
le cuir, leather
curieux, -euse, curious,
    strange

d'abord, at first
le débarquement, landing
débarquer, to land
se décider, to make up one's
    mind
découvert (p.p. of découv-
    rir, to discover)
décrocher, to unhook, pick
    up (telephone receiver)
défendre, to defend; to for-
    bid
le déguisement, disguise
se déguiser (en), to disguise
    oneself (as)
déjà, already
au delà de, beyond

délicieux, -euse, delicious

demain, tomorrow; à demain, till tomorrow

demander, to ask (for)

se demander, to wonder

demeurer, to live

demi, half; huit heures et demie, half past eight

à demi-nu, half-naked

démolir, to demolish

*dénoncer, to denounce

la dent, tooth

dentelé, jagged

le départ, departure

depuis, since

*se déranger to worry, to trouble

dernier, -ière, last; le dernier venu, latest arrival

dérouler, to unroll

derrière, behind

dès que, as soon as

descendre, to go down, get down

désert, empty, deserted

au désespoir, in despair

se déshabiller, to undress

dessus: bras dessus bras dessous, arm in arm

*détruire (*p.p.* détruit), to destroy

deuxième, second

ils devaient (*imp. of* devoir), they had to, were to

devant, in front of; aller devant, to go ahead

*devenir, to become

deviner, to guess

*devoir, to have to

tu devras (*fut. of* devoir)

le diamant, diamond

Mon Dieu! Good Lord!

difficile, difficult

dîner, to dine

le diplomate, diplomat

*dire, to say, tell; dis donc, tell me now

*diriger, to direct

*se diriger, to make one's way

disait (*imp. of* dire)

*disparaître (*imp.* il disparaissait), to disappear

la disparition, disappearance

disparu (*p.p. of* disparaître)

se dissiper, to disappear

dit (*p.p. of* dire)

le doigt, finger (*see also* montrer)

donc, then, therefore

donner, to give; donner sur, to overlook

dont, of whom, whose

*dormir, to sleep

le dos, back

la douane, Customs

le douanier, Customs officer

douce (*f. of* doux), sweet, gentle

doucement, gently

le doute, doubt

la douzaine, dozen

le drame, drama

se dresser, to rise

droit, right; straight

le droit, right

dû (*p.p. of* devoir); il a dû, he had to

l'eau (*f.*), water

écarter, to pull aside

écarlate, scarlet

éclaircir, to clear up, solve

éclairer, to light up, shine on

éclater, to burst; éclater de rire, to burst out laughing

une école, school

écorcher, to graze

s'écouler, to pass (of time)

écouter, to listen (to)

s'écrier, to exclaim, cry

en effet, in fact

*s'élever, to rise

embrasser, to kiss

*emmener, to take away
empêcher, to prevent
emprunter (à), to borrow (from)
en, in, on; some, any; of it, of them
l'encadrement (m.) de la porte, doorway
enchanté, delighted; how do you do
encore, again; yet; still; even
*s'endormir, to fall asleep
un endroit, place, spot
l'enfant (m. and f.), child
enfermé, shut up
enfin, at last
s'enrouler, to coil
ensemble, together
ensuite, next
entassé, piled up
entendre, to hear
un enterrement, burial, funeral
entier, -ière, whole
entre, between
une entrée, entrance
entrer, to enter, come in, go in
*entrevoir, to glimpse
entr'ouvert, half-open
envahir, to invade
envers, towards
envie: avoir envie de, to want to
*envoyer (pres. j'envoie), to send
épatant, wonderful
épouser, to marry
épouvanté, terrified, appalled
éprouver, to experience
une erreur, mistake
un escalier, staircase
*espérer, to hope
un espion, spy

l'espionnage (m.), espionage, spying
un espoir, hope
*essayer, to try
un étage, floor, story
éteint, extinct
s'étendre, to stretch
étendu, lying
étonner, to astonish
un étranger, une étrangère, foreigner; stranger
étranger, -ère, foreign
eu (p.p. of avoir), j'ai eu, I had
eux, them; they
s'évader, to escape
éveiller, to awaken
à l'exception de, except for
s'exclamer, to exclaim
s'excuser, to apologise
un exemple, example; par exemple, for example
expliquer, to explain

faible, weak
*faire, to do; to make; faire venir, to summon; faire passer, to smuggle; faire une surprise, to give a surprise
fait (p.p. of faire); tout à fait, completely
en fait, in fact
il fallait (inf. falloir), it was necessary
la famille, family
le fantôme, ghost
le farceur, joker, wag
il faudra (inf. falloir), it will be necessary
il faut (inf. falloir), it is necessary, you must
le fauteuil, armchair
favori, favourite
la femme, woman; wife
la fenêtre, window

le fer, iron
il fera (*fut. of* faire)
il ferait (*cond. of* faire) (*see Note p.* 14)
le feu, fire
la feuille, leaf; sheet of paper
fier, -ère, proud
la fille, daughter; girl; la jeune fille, girl
la fillette, little girl
la fin, end
fixement: regarder fixement, to stare (at)
le flanc, side
la fleur, flower
le flic, cop (policeman)
flotter, to float
la fois, time, occasion
*se forcer à, to force oneself to
la forêt, forest
la formule, formula
fort, strong; loud; very
fou, mad
la fougère, fern
la foule, crowd
français, French
le français, French (language)
la Française, French woman
frapper, to strike, hit
frissonner, to shudder, shiver
frotter, to rub; se frotter les yeux, to rub one's eyes
la fuite, flight
fumant, smoking
la fumée, smoke
fumer, to smoke
furieux, -euse, furious
le fusil, rifle

le gaillard, lad
galant, gallant, courteous
garder, to guard; to keep
le gardien, guard, keeper
la gare, station
garni, dressed (of food)
gauche, left

le gaz, gas
le gendarme, policeman
le genou, knee
les gens (*m.*), people
gentil, -ille (avec), nice (to)
le geste, gesture
la goélette, schooner
la gorge, throat
goûter, to taste
grave, serious
gravement, solemnly
la grenade lacrymogène, tear-gas bomb
la grimace: faire la grimace, to make a face
grimpant, climbing
grimper (à), to climb (up)
grogner, to grunt
*grommeler, to mutter
gros, big
la guerre, war

habile, capable, clever
habillé de, dressed in
un habitant, inhabitant
habiter, to live (in)
une habitude, habit; avoir l'habitude de, to be in the habit of; d'habitude, usually; que d'habitude, than usual
la hache, axe
haut, high, tall
hein, eh?
hésiter, to hesitate
une heure, hour; o'clock; à tout à l'heure! see you soon!
heureusement, fortunately
heureux, -euse, happy
hier, yesterday
un homme, man
l'humeur (*f.*), mood; de bonne humeur, in a good mood
hurler, to shout
la hutte, hut

un **hydravion**, sea-plane

ici, here; **par ici**, this way
une **idée**, idea
une **île**, island
 il y a, there is, there are; **il y
  avait, il y a eu**, there was,
  there were; **il y aura**, there
  will be; **il y a deux ans**,
  two years ago
 s'imaginer, to imagine
 infranchissable, impassable
 innombrable, innumerable
 inoccupé, unoccupied
 inoffensif, harmless
 inquiet, anxious
 *****s'inquiéter**, to be worried
 l'**inquiétude** (*f.*), anxiety
 intéressant, interesting
 l'**intérieur** (*m.*), interior; **à
  l'intérieur**, inside
 *****interroger**, to interrogate,
  question
 *****interrompre**, to interrupt
 ironiser, to say ironically

 jamais, ever; **ne … jamais**,
  never
la **jetée**, jetty
 *****jeter**, to throw, cast; to throw
  away
 jeudi, Thursday
 jeune, young
 joli, pretty
la **joue**, cheek
 jouer, to play
le **jour**, day
le **journal** (*pl.* **-aux**), news-
  paper
 jovial (*pl.* **-aux**), cheery,
  cheerful
 **Judiciaire: la Police Judi-
  ciaire** (*see Note, p.* 14)
 juin, June
 jusqu'à, as far as, up to;
  until

 là, there; **loin de là**, far
  from it
là-bas, over there
la **lagune**, lagoon
 laisser, to leave; to let;
  laissez-moi faire, leave it
  to me; **laisser tomber**, to
  drop
la **lampe électrique**, torch
 lancer, to throw; to fling
  (a remark)
la **langue**, tongue; language
 large, broad
la **larme**, tear
 léger, -ère, light; slight
 *****léguer**, to bequeath, leave
 lentement, slowly
la **lettre**, letter
 *****lever**, to lift, raise
*****se lever**, to get up
 *****lire**, to read
le **lit**, bed; **au lit**, in bed
 loin, far; **au loin**, in the
  distance
 lointain, distant
 Londres, London
 *****longer**, to skirt
 lorsque, when
 louer, to hire
le **loup**, wolf
 lourdement, heavily
 lui, him; to him, to her; **lui-
  même**, himself
 luisant, gleaming
la **lumière**, light
la **lune**, moon

le **magasin**, shop
la **main**, hand; **à la main**, in
  his, her hand
 maintenant, now
 mal, bad, badly; **faire du
  mal**, to hurt
 malheureux, -euse, un-
  happy
 manquer, to miss

la **marche,** step
marcher, to walk; to go
le **mari,** husband
se **marier,** to get married
marié, married
**maritime: la gare mari-
time,** harbour station
le **masque à gaz,** gas-mask
le **matelot,** sailor
le **matin,** (in the) morning
maudit, cursed, damned
mauvais, bad
meilleur, better, best
***mélanger,** to mix
même, even; same (*see also* **quand**)
***mener,** to lead
***mentir,** to lie
la **mer,** sea
mesdemoiselles, ladies
messieurs, gentlemen;
messieurs-dames, ladies and gentlemen
le **métier,** profession, trade
***mettre,** to put; to put on; se **mettre,** to sit; se **mettre à,** to start to; se **mettre en marche,** to start; se **met-
tre au lit,** to get into bed
les **meubles** (*m.*), furniture
le **meurtre,** murder
le **mien, la mienne,** mine
mieux, better, best; **de mon mieux,** as best I can;
aimer mieux, to prefer
mignon, -onne, sweet
mijoter, to scheme
le **milieu,** middle; **au beau milieu,** right in the middle
des **milliers** (*m.*), thousands
mince, thin, slim
minuit (*m.*), midnight
mis (*p.p. of* **mettre**)
la **mitraillette,** tommy-gun
moins, less; **du moins, au moins,** at least

le **mois,** month
la **moitié,** half; **à moitié caché,** half hidden
le **moment,** moment; **à ce moment-là,** at that moment; **en ce moment,** at the present moment
le **monde,** world; **tout le monde,** everybody
le **monstre,** monster
la **montagne,** mountain; **à la montagne,** in the mountains
monter, to climb; to get (into); to send up
la **montre,** watch
montrer, to show; **montrer du doigt,** to point (at)
mort, dead
la **mort,** death
le **mot,** word
le **moteur,** engine
le **mouchoir,** handkerchief
la **moue: faire une moue,** to pout
le **moyen,** way, means
le **mur,** wall
le **mystère,** mystery
mystérieusement, mysteri-
ously

la **naissance,** birth
naturellement, naturally
ne (*see* **aucun, jamais, personne, plus, que, rien**)
le **nez,** nose
ni, neither; nor; or
le **niveau,** level
noir, black
la **noix de coco,** coconut
nommer, to name
nouvelle (*f. of* **nouveau**), new
les **nouvelles** (*f.*), news
nu, naked
le **nuage,** cloud

la nuit, night
le numéro, number

obéir, to obey
l'obscurité (*f.*), darkness
observer: faire observer,
to remark
*offrir, to offer
un oiseau, bird
à l'ombre (*f.*) de, in the shade of
une ombrelle, sunshade, (café)
umbrella
on, one, they
orangé, orange-coloured
un ordre, order; à vos ordres,
at your service
oser, to dare
ou, or: ou ... ou, either ...
or
où, where
oublier, to forget
en outre, moreover, besides
ouvert (*p.p. of* ouvrir), open
*(s')ouvrir, to open

pacifique, peaceful
le palmier, palm tree
le papier, paper
par, by; through
*paraître (*pres.* il paraît), to
appear
pareil, similar; rien de
pareil, nothing like it
parfait, perfect; fine!
parler, to speak; parlons,
let us speak
parmi, among
la parole, word; couper la
parole à, to interrupt
la partie, part
*partir (*pres.* il part), to
depart
partout, everywhere
le pas, footstep; à quelques
pas, a few yards away
le passe-partout, skeleton key

passer, to pass; to go; to
spend
se passer, to happen; qu'est-
ce qui se passe? what's
going on?
le patron, owner, boss
le paysage, landscape
la peau, skin
la pêche, fishing
pêcher, to fish
le pêcheur, fisherman
la peine, difficulty, trouble; à
peine, scarcely
pendant, during; pendant
que, while
*pénétrer, to penetrate, go
(into)
la pensée, thought
penser (à), to think (of)
perdre, to lose
la perle, pearl
*permettre, to permit, allow
le personnage, person, character
personne ... (ne), nobody
persuadé, sure
à perte de vue, out of sight
petit, little; lad; mon petit,
my dear
peu, little; peu à peu, little
by little
la peur, fear; avoir peur, to be
frightened
peut-être, perhaps
je peux (*pres. of* pouvoir)
le pic, peak
le pied, foot; à pied, on foot;
prendre pied, to set foot
piquer, to bite, sting
la piste, track; runway
la place, square; seat
la plage, beach
plaisanter, to joke
plaît: s'il vous plaît, if you
please
plat, flat

plein, full
pleurer, to cry, weep
***plonger,** to plunge, thrust
plus (de), more; **ne … plus,** no longer; **de plus en plus,** more and more; **le plus,** the most; **plus de cent,** more than a hundred; **sans un mot de plus,** without another word
plusieurs, several
plutôt, rather
la **poche,** pocket
le **point,** point; **sur le point de,** about to
la **pointe,** point; **sur la pointe des pieds,** on tip-toe
le **poisson,** fish
le **policier,** policeman
le **port,** harbour
la **porte,** door
le **portefeuille,** wallet
porter, to carry; to wear
la **portière,** door (of car, train, etc.)
poster, to post, station
pour, for; in order to
pourrez; vous pourrez (*fut. of* **pouvoir**)
pousser, to push; utter
la **poussière,** dust
***pouvoir,** to be able
se **précipiter,** to rush forward
précis, exactly, sharp
premier, -ère, first
***prendre,** to take
près de, near; **de plus près,** closer to
présenter, to introduce
se **présenter,** to present oneself, arrive
presque, almost
pressant: d'une voix pressante, urgently
le **pressentiment,** presentiment

prêt, ready
prêter, to lend
prier, to beg; **je vous en prie,** please, don't mention it
pris (*p.p. of* **prendre**)
proche, near
profond, deep
*se **promener,** to go for a walk
promis (*p.p. of* **promettre,** to promise)
***prononcer,** to declare
proposer, to suggest
la **propriété,** property, estate
pu, *p.p. of* **pouvoir**
puis, then
puisque, since
la **puissance,** power

le **quai,** platform; quay; river embankment
quand, when; **quand même,** all the same
qu'as-tu? qu'avez-vous? what's the matter?
que, that, which; what; than; **ne … que,** only
quel, quelle, what
quelque, some
quelquefois, sometimes
quelques-uns, quelques-unes, some
quelqu'un, someone
qu'est-ce que? qu'est-ce qui? what?
qui, who; whom; which; **qui est-ce qui?** who?
quitter, to leave
quoi, what; which; **sans quoi,** otherwise

raccrocher, to hang up, put back (receiver)
raconter, to tell
la **raison,** reason; **avoir raison,** to be right

raisonnable, sensible
le rapide, express train
raser, to raze to the ground;
    to skim over
ravi, delighted
ravissant, delightful
le rayon, beam; shelf
réaction: avion à réaction,
    jet plane
récemment, recently
le récepteur, receiver (phone)
la recherche, les recherches,
    search; à la recherche de,
    in search of
le récif, reef
  *reconnaître, to recognise
    reconnu (*p.p.* of recon-
    naître)
  *recueillir, to gather
    redescendre, to go, get
    down again
se refermer, to close again
    réfléchir, to think
le regard, look, glance
    regarder, to look (at), to
    watch
je regrette, I'm sorry
*se relever, to get up again
    remarquer, to notice; to
    remark
  *remplacer, to put back
le rendez-vous: avoir rendez-
    vous, to have a date
    rendre, to give back; rendre
    visite, to pay a visit; se
    rendre, to go
  *renoncer à, to give up
des renseignements, (m.), i-n
    formation
se renseigner sur, to make
    enquiries about
    rentrer, to return
  *reparaître (*p.p.* reparu), to
    reappear
le repas, meal; faire un repas,
    to have a meal

*répéter, to repeat
    repliquer, to retort, answer
    back
    répondre, to reply
    repris (*p.p.* of reprendre, to
    resume)
le requin, shark
    respirer, to breathe
    ressembler à, to resemble,
    look like
le reste, the rest; du reste,
    besides
    rester, to remain; il reste,
    there remains
se retirer, to withdraw, retire
    retourner, to return
se retourner, to turn round
    retrouver, to find again
    réussir, to succeed
le rêve, dream
    revendre, to sell again
  *revenir, to return
    rêver, to dream
je reviendrai (*fut.* of revenir)
  *revoir, to see again
le rhum, rum
le rideau, curtain; screen
    rider, to ruffle
    rien, nothing; rien que,
    nothing but; ne . . . rien,
    nothing, not anything
  *rire, to laugh
le risque, risk
la rive, bank (of river)
la robe, dress
le rocher, rock
  *rompre, to break
le ronron, purring, humming
    rouge, red
    rougir, to blush
le rouleau, roll
    rouler, to roll; to travel
la route, road; changer de
    route, to change direction
la rue, street
la ruse, trick

le **Russe,** Russian

le **sable,** sand
le **sac,** bag
sale, dirty
la **salle,** room
sans, without
je **saurais** (*cond. of* **savoir**) (*see Note, p.* 14)
sauter, to jump
se **sauver,** to escape
*__savoir__ (*pres.* **je sais, ils savent**), to know
savoureux, -euse, tasty
se, himself, herself, themselves; to himself, etc.
la **semaine,** week
semblable, similar
semblant: faire semblant de, to pretend
sembler, to seem
semé de, strewn with
la **sentinelle,** sentry
*se **sentir,** to feel
il **sera** (*fut. of* **être**)
il **serait, nous serions** (*cond. of* **être**) (*see Note, p.* 14)
le **serpent,** snake
serrer, to press tightly; **serrer la main à,** to shake hands with
la **serveuse,** waitress
de **service,** on duty
*se **servir de,** to make use of
seul, single (one), only
si, if; so; yes
siffler, to whistle; to hiss
le **signe,** sign; **faire signe que oui,** to nod
la **silhouette,** silhouette, outline
sinon, if not, otherwise
situé, situated
sixième, sixth
la **sœur,** sister

la **soif,** thirst; **avoir soif,** to be thirsty
le **soin,** care
le **soir,** evening
sois (*imperative of* **être**), be
le **soleil,** sun
le **sommeil,** sleep
le **sommet,** top, summit
*__songer,__ to dream, think
la **sorcière,** witch
*__sortir,__ to go out, leave; to take out
soudain, suddenly
souffler, to whisper; to blow
*__soulever,__ to raise
le **soupçon,** suspicion
le **soupir,** sigh
soupirer, to sigh
(en) **souriant,** smiling
*__sourire,__ to smile
sous, under
le **spectacle,** sight
succulent, juicy
suis (*imperative of* **suivre**): **suis-le,** follow him
suisse, Swiss
la **Suissesse,** Swiss woman
suite: tout de suite, at once
*__suivre,__ to follow; **suivi de,** followed by
sûr, sure
sur-le-champ, on the spot
surpris, surprised
surtout, above all
survoler, to fly over
sympathique, likeable

tais-toi (*imperative of* **se taire**), be quiet
tandis que, while, whereas
tant (de), so much, so many; **tant mieux,** so much the better, good!
tard, late
le **téléphone,** telephone; **au**

téléphone, on the telephone

le temps, time; weather; à temps, in time; de temps en temps, from time to time; en même temps, at the same time

tendre, to stretch; to hand

*tenir, to hold; se tenir, to stand

le terrain, ground

la terrasse, terrace; en terrasse, terraced, flat

la terre, earth, ground; à terre, to the ground; par terre, on the ground

la tête, head

tiendrez: vous tiendrez (*fut. of* tenir)

tiens! well, well!

tirer, to draw, pull

toi, you

le toit, roof

le ton, tone (of voice); sur un ton furieux, furiously

la topaze, topaz (semi-precious stone)

le torrent, mountain stream

tortueux, -euse, winding

tôt, early; le plus tôt possible, as early as possible

toujours, always; still

(se) tourner, to turn; to turn out (well, badly, etc.)

tous (*pl. of* tout), all; tous les trois, all three of them

tout, all, every; everything; very; toutes les dix secondes, every ten seconds; toutes les trois, all three of them (*see also* coup, fait, heure, monde, suite)

en train de, in the act of

le traître, traitor

tranquillement, quietly

la trappe, trap-door

à travers, through, across

traverser, to cross

triste, sad

se tromper, to be mistaken

trop (de), too; too much

le trou, hole

trouver, to find; se trouver, to be

tu (*p.p. of* se taire, to fall silent)

tuer, to kill

utiliser, to use

il va, tu vas (*pres. of* aller)

les vacances (*f.*), holidays

la valise, suitcase

la vallée, valley

*se venger, to take revenge

*venir, to come; venir de, to have just

le vent, wind

le verre, glass

vers, towards

il veut (*pres. of* vouloir)

la vie, life

vieille (*f. of* vieux), old

il viendra (*fut. of* venir)

je viens (*pres. of* venir)

vieux, old; mon vieux, my dear fellow

la ville, town

le vin, wine

violet, -ette, purple

le visage, face

visiter, to visit; to examine

il vit (*pres. of* vivre)

la vitesse, speed; à toute vitesse, at full speed

*vivre, to live

voici, here is

voilà, there is

*voir, to see

voisin, neighbouring

le **voisin,** neighbour

la **voiture,** carriage, car; **en voiture,** by car (*see also Note, p.* 7)

la **voix,** voice; **à voix basse,** in a low voice

le **vol,** flight; **vol régulier,** regular service flight

le **volcan,** volcano

voler, to steal

le **volet,** shutter

le **voleur,** thief

ils **vont** (*pres. of* **aller**)

voudriez, voudrions: nous voudrions, vous voud- **riez** (*cond. of* **vouloir**), we, you would like

***vouloir,** to wish, want; **vouloir dire,** to mean; **si vous voulez (bien),** if you will

il **voyait** (*imp. of* **voir**)

voulu (*p.p. of* **vouloir**)

vrai, real, true

vraiment, really

vu (*p.p. of* **voir**)

y, there; in it, in them

yeux (*pl. of* **un œil**), eyes

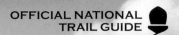

Yorkshire Wolds Way

Tony Gowers
and Roger Ratcliffe

Aurum

in association with

NATURAL
ENGLAND

Acknowledgements

I would like to thank Malcolm Hodgson, Trail Officer for the Yorkshire Wolds Way, and Pat Wharam of East Riding Council for sharing their knowledge of the trail; Roger Ratcliffe for much of the trail history and the route description; Don Lee of the Larkin Society; Paul Schofield, the Hull walks guide; and Rose Horspool of the Yorkshire Wolds Heritage Centre. I would also like to say a big thank you to my partner Val and Fudge the dog, who supported me on my Yorkshire travels. – *Tony Gowers*

This fully revised and updated edition first published 2013
First published as *Wolds Way* 1992 by Aurum Press Ltd.

Text copyright © 1992, 2004, 2007, 2011 Aurum Press Ltd.
New material copyright © 2013 Tony Gowers

Aurum Press Ltd, 74–77 White Lion Street, London N1 9PF • www.aurumpress.co.uk
in association with Natural England • www.naturalengland.org.uk

Photographs copyright ©2013 the photographer or agency as follows: pages 1, 17, 28–9, 55, 104–5 and 128 Mike Kipling; 15 Tessa Bunney; 6–7, 8, 12–7, 13, 32–3, 35, 45, 47, 49, 52, 67, 82 (bottom), 100, 110 and 117 Tony Gowers; 2–3, 21–2, 24, 25, 26, 31, 36, 38, 48, 64, 69, 76–7, 78, 86–7, 90, 92, 96, 97 (top), 106, 113, 119, 120, 125, 133 and 136–7 Alamy; 27 (top) Getty Images; 27 (bottom) Topfoto; 97 (bottom) Dave Webster; 108 Wolds Way Lavender; 123 Flickr; all other photographs copyright © Ian Carstairs. Page 82 David Hockney: *Warter Vista* 2006; oil on 2 canvases (48 x 36" each); 48 x 72" overall; © David Hockney; photo credit Richard Schmidt. Page 83 David Hockney: *Bigger Trees near Warter or/ou Peinture sur le Motif pour le Nouvel Age Post-Photographique* 2007; oil on 50 canvases (36 x 48" each); 180 x 480" overall; © David Hockney; Collection Tate, London; photo credit Richard Schmidt.

This product includes mapping data licensed from Ordnance Survey® with the permission of the Controller of Her Majesty's Stationery Office. © Crown copyright 2013. All rights reserved. Licence number 43453U.
Ordnance Survey and Travelmaster are registered trademarks and the Ordnance Survey symbol and Explorer are trademarks of Ordnance Survey, the national mapping agency of Great Britain.

ISBN 978 1 78131 064 9

Book design by Robert Updegraff
Printed and bound in China

Cover photograph: *The village of Millington seen from Harmer Hill*
Half-title photograph: *Poppies in rape field near Thixendale*
Title-page photograph: *Horse Dale near Pocklington*

Aurum Press want to ensure that these National Trail Guides are always as up to date as possible – but stiles collapse, pubs close and bus services change all the time. If, on walking this path, you discover any important changes that future walkers need to be aware of, do let us know. Either email us on **trailguides@aurumpress.co.uk** with your comments, or, if you take the trouble to drop us a line to:

Trail Guides, Aurum Press, 74–77 White Lion Street, London N1 9PF,

we'll send you a free guide of your choice as thanks.

Contents

Contact details • Travel information • Accommodation • Tourist information •
Walking holiday providers for the Yorkshire Wolds Way • Other contacts •
Further reading • Ordnance Survey Maps covering Yorkshire Wolds Way •
YWW Official Completion Book

Shorter walks appear on pages 50, 80, 130 and 134

How to use this guide

This guide to the 79-mile (127-km) Yorkshire Wolds Way is in three parts:
- The introduction, with an historical background to the area and advice for walkers.
- The Way itself, split into six chapters, with maps opposite the description for each route section. The distances noted with each chapter represent the total length of the Yorkshire Wolds Way, including sections through towns and villages. This part of the guide also includes information on places of interest as well as four shorter walks further afield. Key sites are numbered both in the text and on the maps to make it easier to follow the route description.
- The last part includes useful information such as local transport, accommodation and organisations involved with the Yorkshire Wolds Way.

The maps have been prepared by the Ordnance Survey for this Trail Guide using 1:25 000 Explorer™ maps as a base. The line of the Yorkshire Wolds Way is shown in yellow, with the status of each section of the trail – footpath or bridleway, for example – shown in green underneath (see key on inside front cover). These rights-of-way markings also indicate the precise alignment of the Yorkshire Wolds Way, which you should follow. In some cases, the yellow line on these maps may show a route that is different from that shown on older maps; you are recommended to follow the yellow route in this guide, which will be the route that is waymarked with the distinctive acorn symbol ● used for all National Trails. Any parts of the Yorkshire Wolds Way that may be difficult to follow on the ground are clearly highlighted in the route description, and important points to watch for are marked with letters in each chapter, both in the text and on the maps.
Some maps start on a right-hand page and continue on the left-hand page – black arrows (➤) at the edge of the maps indicate the start point.

Should there be a need to divert the Yorkshire Wolds Way from the route shown in this guide, for maintenance work or because the route has had to be changed, you are advised to follow any waymarks or signs along the path.

Distance checklist

This list will assist you in calculating the distances between your proposed overnight accommodation and in checking your progress along the walk.

location	approx. distance from previous location	
	miles	km
Hessle	0	0
North Ferriby	3.1	5.0
Welton	3.5	5.6
Brantingham	4.2	6.7
South Cave	2.1	3.4
Newbald	5.2	8.4
Goodmanham	5.8	9.3
Londesborough	2.4	3.9
*Market Weighton (from Newbald)**	*6.7*	*10.8*
*Londesborough (from Market Weighton)**	*2.7*	*4.3*
Nunburnholme	2.5	4.0
Millington	2.7	4.3
Huggate	5.9	9.5
Fridaythorpe	2.5	4.0
Thixendale	4.1	6.6
Wharram le Street	5.3	8.5
Settrington Beacon	3.7	6.0
Wintringham	2.7	4.3
Sherburn	6.8	10.9
Ganton	3.0	4.8
Staxton Wold	3.2	5.1
Muston	6.5	10.5
Filey Brigg	2.5	4.0

* Alternative route

An arable field near Ganton on the northern part of the trail in late summer.

An avenue of gnarled old trees on the
trail between Ganton and Staxton.

Key map 2

Chalk outcrops at Fairydale near Fridaythorpe in the Yorkshire Wolds.

PART ONE
Introduction

Lovers of unspoilt countryside in northern England need look no further than the Yorkshire Wolds. These peaceful, rolling chalk hills with their deep green valleys are tucked away off the beaten track in the East Riding. Few tourists hog the narrow lanes, crowds of walkers are rarely encountered, while the attractive Wolds villages are unlikely to be made up of second homes or holiday cottages. However, the recent success of the artist David Hockney's Royal Academy exhibition, *A Bigger Picture*, which showcased the Yorkshire Wolds, has undoubtedly introduced a wider audience to the beauty of this landscape.

There is no better way to discover this fascinating area than by following the Yorkshire Wolds Way along its 79 miles (127 km) from Hessle, beside the Humber, to the airy cliffs above Filey. On the way you will pass one of the best-preserved deserted medieval settlements in the country, attractive villages, large country estates, and dry valleys which have remained unchanged for centuries. Away from the trail itself, this guide also includes other interesting places to visit in East Yorkshire, ranging from estate villages and the historic port of Hull to the magnificence of the minsters at York and Beverley and the remote 'end of the world' feel of the Holderness Peninsula.

As well as being the ideal introduction to this relatively undiscovered part of eastern England, the Yorkshire Wolds Way National Trail is a great choice for

newcomers to long-distance walking. Each section is suitable to every level of walking ability.

The book also contains some additional shorter walks. These range from a circular walk in the heart of the Wolds amongst the landscape that inspired David Hockney (see page 80) and a Philip Larkin literary walk in Hull (see page 50), to a stroll through the fascinating old parts of Bridlington (see page 130) and a magnificent clifftop ramble around Flamborough Head – a fitting finale to your Yorkshire Wolds Way experience (see page 134). A useful map showing the Sykes churches of the Yorkshire Wolds is included (page 94).

The Yorkshire Wolds Way story

The formation of long-distance footpaths in England and Wales was very much a product of the 1960s expansion of leisure time, disposable income and interest in the countryside. Following the Pennine Way's opening in 1965, there was pressure from ramblers for a number of other routes that would traverse a range of hills while linking a series of historic and scenic treasures.

The Wolds Way, as it was called until the word 'Yorkshire' was added to the title in 2003, was one such continuous footpath. The idea came from the Ramblers' Association, East Yorkshire and Derwent Area, whose members had long appreciated the beauties of the Yorkshire Wolds. Their proposal was put to the National Parks Commission (forerunner of the Countryside Commission – now Natural England) in 1967 and within a year it had been approved in principle by the new Commission and by the East Riding County Council. The route would begin on the Humber shore at North Ferriby and finish at the East Riding county boundary just north of Filey Brigg.

The first section to open was a 4-mile (6.5-km) path through Goodmanham and Londesborough, which was officially inaugurated by Lord Halifax, then Lord Lieutenant of the East Riding, in November 1973. But it was not until 26 July 1977 that the Countryside Commission formally proposed a complete route. It had taken 10 years to get just one small stretch of the National Trail officially opened and waymarked; it was to take another five years to get agreement over the rest of the Yorkshire Wolds Way.

The route that was finally agreed included an extension to Hessle Haven, at its southernmost end, and a link with Market Weighton. The most difficult sections to secure were at the northern end, between Thixendale and Filey, and about 10 miles of new rights-of-way had to be created. At last, the official route was opened on 2 October 1982, at a ceremony performed by a major Wolds landowner, Lord Middleton, at Fridaythorpe, which is the approximate halfway point on the 79-mile (127-km) trail.

The Yorkshire Wolds Way recently celebrated its 30th anniversary with a series of walks organised by the East Yorkshire and Derwent Area Ramblers.

Woodland aconites are amongst the first flowers to appear in early spring.

A northerly chalk landscape

Chalk underlies virtually all of the Yorkshire Wolds Way. Only the final stretch of walking on the boulder-clay cliffs at Filey, and the anomalous black reef of lower calcareous gritstone that forms Filey Brigg, provide a contrast in scenery.

The Yorkshire Wolds are, in fact, the northernmost extremity of a continuous band of chalk that extends across the country in two directions from Dorset. The first thrust heads eastwards to form such national landmarks as the Seven Sisters and the White Cliffs of Dover, while passing through Sussex, Surrey and Kent as the South and North Downs. The second heads north-eastwards through Wiltshire, Berkshire and the Chiltern Hills of Buckinghamshire, then up through Norfolk; it disappears from view at The Wash to reappear as the Lincolnshire Wolds. Cut by the mighty Humber, the chalk finally emerges to create the Yorkshire Wolds, which stretch north as far as Muston Wold, the most northerly chalk in Europe, before terminating at the high-rise seabird colonies of Bempton Cliffs (see page 120) and the scenic *pièce de résistance* of Flamborough Head (see page 120).

Chalk was formed between 65 and 145 million years ago and is composed of the bones and shells of countless minute creatures that accumulated when earth movements reduced the sea level over the infant British landscape. The white mud compressed and hardened, and was squeezed and eroded by volcanic action and the creation of new rivers. The final polish of softly rounded hills and dry

valleys was provided by the last Ice Age. And the rest of what we know today as classic English chalk downland scenery was formed by people – the sweet chalk pastures, the steep meadow banks, the well-cultivated and grazed terrain of some of the most fertile land in Europe.

Water is quickly absorbed by chalk, which means that conditions underfoot are never wet for long because the land quickly dries out after rain. This has led to the creation of the most classic and dramatic feature of this type of landscape – the dry valley. You will pass through countryside with many superb examples on your walk. This absorption also deprives the landscape of many springs and water courses. A curious characteristic of chalk downland is the streams that usually run underground but occasionally break to the surface. In the Yorkshire Wolds they are known as 'races', the best-known being the Gypsey Race, which runs from Duggleby, just off the Yorkshire Wolds Way, to Bridlington. In southern and western England they are known as 'bournes'. However, in this part of the country water abstraction has meant that the 'races' are a much rarer sight now than they once were.

The Yorkshire Wolds over the centuries

Some of the oldest cultivated landscape is to be found in chalk downs. Mesolithic tribes from the Continent arrived in southern England about 10,000 years ago as the ice sheets melted and spread north. They lived off the fish and wild animals to be found in the Vale of Pickering to the north of the Wolds.

No water has flowed down these valleys for thousands of years, while today the chalk will easily absorb all the rain that falls here.

Introduction

Around 3250 BC came yet more invaders from the Mediterranean, bringing with them the earliest farming skills. They had no need for the hunting grounds of marshes but colonised the fertile hills, developing a patchwork of small fields. Thus the Wolds, which have so few habitations today, were very much alive 4,000 years ago. Later settlers arrived from France, tribes of warriors with chieftains whose remains were buried with chariots in great barrows – their main legacy to today's landscape. The largest barrow is Duggleby Howe (see pages 99 and 106), located just off the Yorkshire Wolds Way near Wharram le Street. Other barrows are Staple Howe, just off the trail in the Knapton Plantation, and Willy Howe near Thwing.

The Romans arrived in about AD 71. Their principal camp was west of the Wolds at Eboracum, the embryonic city of York. They also built a signal station above Filey Brigg, at the end of the Yorkshire Wolds Way, to raise the alarm

should the Angles invade from the sea. Indeed, the Angles did just that in the 5th century, but by then the Romans had finished with Britain.

The Saxons, and later the Danes, laid the foundation for much of what you see in the Wolds today – names like Brantingham and Goodmanham are Saxon, while the numerous villages and farm names ending in 'by' and 'thorpe' are a reminder of the Danes. It is thought that many field boundaries, still in use, were first laid out by these pre-Conquest settlers.

Early medieval times were a turbulent period in the area's history. Many people were driven off the land by the Norman barons. The Black Death also caused thousands of casualties and virtually wiped out some settlements, the most famous being Wharram Percy (see 'Deserted villages', page 19). Later, the Land Enclosures meant that the Wolds were turned over to sheep-rearing. Cereal-growing, which is the dominant

The fine Norman doorway of St Nicholas Church,
situated in the village of North Newbald.

agricultural activity today, began in the 18th century. Since that time hedges may have been grubbed out to enlarge a field but, essentially, you will be walking through a landscape pretty much unchanged for over 200 years (see 'Farming', page 23).

Deserted medieval villages

The Yorkshire Wolds are full of sites of lost medieval villages which have been deserted for many years. The reasons they were abandoned during the Middle Ages can vary, but common factors were crop failures on less fertile lands forcing the population to seek better locations, depopulation of a village after the Black Death, or movements as a result of the Enclosures of common land. Many of these sites today are scarcely noticeable on the ground except for a few earthworks and crop marks. However, one of the best-preserved deserted medieval villages in the country is at Wharram Percy, a site maintained by English Heritage, which can be found on the Yorkshire Wolds Way between Thixendale and Sherburn. If walking that section in a day, try to allow at least an hour to explore and savour the peace of this tranquil place. Close your eyes and allow your imagination to wander . . .

Wharram Percy (Wharram is derived from the old Scandinavian *hwerhamm*, which means 'at the bends', while the Percys were lords of the manor in the 12th–14th centuries) was built in the beautifully tranquil Deep Dale. There is evidence of at least one Iron Age house (*c.*100 BC) having existed here, as well as a Roman farm or villa, but the village grew under Anglo-Saxon settlers. For three centuries it was a compact farming village, with 30 households, a population of 150, a church and a cemetery. However, by the mid-14th century a combination of the Black Death and a change from corn-growing to sheep-rearing saw its population cut by half. The last house was deserted around the year 1500.

Today, Wharram Percy is mainly a collection of bumpy earthworks. St Martin's Church contains much of its original 12th-century materials and is the most visible relic. Most of the village was on the hillside to the west and north of the church, and it is possible to make out the grassed-over foundations of peasant houses, a manor house and a mill. There is also a reconstructed pond.

Locations for the many other deserted medieval settlements in the Yorkshire Wolds can be much harder to spot. The Yorkshire Wolds Way passes close to one of them, Towthorpe on the Market Weighton loop (see page 70); and The Camp, on the final stage of the walk east of Sherburn, is the site of an abandoned settlement (see page 126). In both places it is just possible to make out a few remains in the form of earthworks.

Other deserted village sites in the Yorkshire Wolds include East Heslerton, just north of the trail; Riplingham, near South Cave; and neighbouring Cottam and Cowlam close to Sledmere. The eerie ruins of Cottam Chapel are attractively located in Cottam Well Dale, while nearby Cowlam became abandoned after the Black Death. Both can be visited on a circular walk following minor roads and bridleways, starting from the enormous and impressive Sykes Monument on the B1252 south of Sledmere.

Attractive thatched cottages in front of the War Memorial in the estate village of Warter.

Large country estates

One of the curiosities of the Yorkshire Wolds is the large number of vast estates, some of which contain whole villages, which are still privately owned. In some cases these families are the descendants of the people who enclosed the land between 1750 and 1850, thus creating an agricultural landscape which remains virtually unchanged to this day.

Walking from south to north on the trail, you will pass through or close to the following country estates:

Londesborough Estate

The Yorkshire Wolds Way passes through the Londesborough Estate between Goodmanham and Millington. The attractive parklands have a long history and are thought to have been the site of a Roman settlement called Delgovita. A mansion was built here in the 16th

century and the estate was owned by the powerful Clifford family. Henry Clifford was a friend of Henry VIII and became the first Earl of Cumberland, a title that became extinct in 1643. The Burlington family, under the Earl of Burlington, created the lakes and landscaped parkland, while the 6th Duke of Devonshire developed the Wolds farms at the time of the Enclosures. George Hudson, the famous 'Railway King' of the 19th century, bought the estate in 1845. In 1827, on the eve of the railway boom, he had invested a £30,000 inheritance in railway shares and then helped to gain parliamentary approval for the York and North Midland Railway. Three times Lord Mayor of York, he made the city the railway capital of England and bought the Londesborough Estate at the height of his success. He even went as far as constructing his own private railway station for the estate, though it has long been demolished. Hudson's reputation was ruined in 1849

when he was accused of fraud. The Hudson Way is now a recreational route along the disused line between Market Weighton and Beverley (see 'Other trails', page 31).

The Londesborough Estate has subsequently been owned by the Denisons, a banking family, and remains in private ownership today. (See also pages 66–7.)

Dalton Estate

The village of South Dalton and the Dalton Estate lie to the east of the Yorkshire Wolds Way from the Londesborough area. The 18th-century hall is still owned by Lord Hotham, whose family have owned the land for generations. The spire of St Mary's Church dominates the local area and the dining pub the Pipe and Glass, which is located on the site of the original gatehouse to the estate, is an extremely popular eating venue.

Warter Estate

Warter (see page 68) is an attractive estate village located east of the Yorkshire Wolds Way near Kilnwick Percy. Here an Augustinian priory was founded in 1132 by Geoffrey Fitzpain, who owned much of the land here in the Middle Ages. The priory was dissolved in 1536 as part of the Tudor rebellion by the people of Yorkshire against Henry VIII known as the Pilgrimage of Grace. This famous event has been commemorated in a new walking route called the Pilgrimage of Grace Heritage Walk (see 'Other trails', page 31). The dissolved priory estate was acquired by the Pennington family of Muncaster and Warter Priory was rebuilt. Over the years shooting parties on the estate have attracted politicians, including Winston Churchill, and nobility. In 1998 the estate and most of the village houses were purchased by the current owner.

Sledmere Estate

Sledmere village (see page 100) and the Sledmere Estate are located about 6 miles (9.6 km) east of the Wharram Percy section of the Yorkshire Wolds Way. Sledmere has been the family home of the Sykes for more than 250 years. The family amassed a fortune from shipping, finance and the flourishing Baltic trade in pig iron when Richard Sykes married Mary Kirkby, co-heiress of the Sledmere Estate. His nephew, Christopher, extended the house, landscaped the grounds and planted 1,000 acres of trees, eventually leaving 30,000 acres of farmland and around 80 tenanted farms. It was the Sykes family that was mainly responsible for turning the pastoral countryside into prime arable land. The 5th baronet, Sir Tatton Sykes, financed the restoration of many local churches in the area (see below).

The main house was gutted by fire in 1911, although villagers helped save most of the contents. So successfully restored was it, however, over the following five years that it still seems a beautiful Georgian gem with fine rooms, including the fabulous blue-tiled Turkish room created for Sir Mark Sykes, the 6th Baronet and eminent orientalist.

It was Sir Mark who founded the Wagoners Special Reserve, turning 1,000 local farmers, blacksmiths and saddlers into a unit which was among the first to go to France in the First World War to drive horse-drawn supply wagons. There is a museum to their moving story in Seldmere House and a monument to their achievements stands on the road through the village, a scene captured by Hockney in a 1997 painting.

Sledmere village is an attractive place to visit and the magnificent Sledmere House and gardens are open to the public.

Settrington Estate

The Yorkshire Wolds Way passes close to the eastern fringes of the Settrington Estate on the section between Wharram le Street and Wintringham. Settrington village today is a peaceful and picturesque place, but has become much reduced in size over the years. The manor and estate have experienced a succession of owners, including Margaret Douglas, Countess of Lennox and niece to Henry VIII, who was considered a threat to Queen Elizabeth I.

Scampston Estate

The estate is located close to the Yorkshire Wolds Way near Wintringham, on the Thixendale to Sherburn section. Along with the Lowthorpe and Harpham Estates near Driffield, the Scampston Estate has been owned and managed by the Legard family and their St Quintin ancestors for generations. Scampston Hall dates from 1700 and has magnificent Regency interiors. The park was designed by Capability Brown and the walled garden was created by the eminent Dutch designer Piet Oudolf. The Hall, park and gardens are all open to the public.

Sykes churches

There is a superb range of churches in the Yorkshire Wolds, many of them built or rebuilt by Sir Tatton Sykes of Sledmere between 1866 and 1913. A Sykes Churches Trail (north and south) has been established by the East Yorkshire Historic Churches Trust to enable visitors to see a selection of these wonderful buildings (see page 94).

Ripening barley along the western escarpment of the Yorkshire Wolds.

Farming

The Yorkshire Wolds is one of the most intensively farmed areas of Britain. About 95 per cent of the land is arable, the main production being cereal crops such as winter and spring/winter barley. About one third of the Wolds comprises grazing pastures or oilseed rape production, with a smaller acreage devoted to pea-vining. Among the most visually dramatic features in the landscape are the great yellow sheets of oilseed rape along the route in spring and early summer. The soil quality, although good throughout the Wolds, is richest on the southernmost slopes fronting the Humber. The loam is medium to heavy, and the presence of large numbers of chalk stones and pebbles keeps it well drained.

Arable farming, though, is a relatively recent phenomenon. Most of the land seen on the tops today was at one time a vast, grassy sheep walk. Some sections survive – usually close to the steep banks that ploughs cannot reach. One of the last surviving sheep walks was at Millington Pasture, which was finally enclosed for cultivation in the 1960s. Sheep continue to be the principal livestock of the Wolds, with up to 200,000 lambs and ewes being herded. The Wolds are also used for dairy and beef cattle production, and the predominant breeds are black-and-white Friesian and Holstein, with a few herds of Charolais and Limousin.

Many of today's field boundaries follow the lines of ring-fences and ditches, used to keep flocks together, and this explains why some fields are positively vast. As well as large fields there are some extremely large farms in the Yorkshire Wolds. These were created during the Enclosures of 1750–1850. Smaller farmsteads exist only beside the villages.

Wildlife of the Yorkshire Wolds

Along the Humber Estuary

Take your time, if you can, on the first stretch of the Yorkshire Wolds Way, as it is here that the greatest variety of birdlife may be seen. The Humber is recognised as one of the most important bird-feeding grounds on the east coast. Wading birds that are present at most times of the year include dunlin, redshank and oystercatcher, joined at the spring and autumn migration periods by large numbers of knot, sanderling, curlew, grey and ringed plover and bar-tailed godwit. Species of duck include mallard and shelduck, plus the occasional teal and wigeon. In addition, some 10,000 pink-footed geese winter annually up the Humber Estuary and some wander downstream. The shoreline between the bridge and North Ferriby is patrolled by short-eared owls and kestrels. The Humber Bridge Country Park beside the bridge is a good place to view the common species of warblers in spring and summer.

The increasingly rare water vole makes its home amongst the reed beds along the River Humber.

Reed beds along the estuary provide an ideal habitat for two increasingly rare species – the bittern and the water vole. You may be lucky enough to spot a grey seal in the waters of the Humber Estuary.

On the chalk downland

The vast majority of your walk will be away from the coast amongst the magnificent scenery of chalk downland. This habitat has some of the most distinctive flora and fauna in the British landscape. Well-drained banks and fields with calcium-rich soils in areas like the Yorkshire Wolds provide ideal conditions for flowers that require lime for their survival, such as harebells, cowslips, buttercups, shepherd's purse, wild thyme and wild basil. Other flowers to be found include salad burnet, common rockrose, common milkwort, burnet saxifrage, clustered bellflower, dropwort, field scabious, small scabious, crested hair-grass and quaking grass. Orchids are less prevalent than on southern slopes, but include pyramidal, bee, green-winged and frog varieties. A dramatic splash of summer colour is provided by blood-red poppies that thrive in the difficult corners out of reach of the plough.

These wild flowers, in turn, attract colourful butterflies in summer, like the familiar orange tip, red admiral and the common blue. Other species of butterfly to be found on the downs are the marbled white, brown argus, grayling and dingy skipper, while you may spot cistus forester and forester moths too. The uncultivated grasses provide perfect nesting places for skylarks, while the seeds of tall grasses make ideal food for goldfinches. There are bank voles – which, of course, attract the kestrel – and stoats, while weasels lurk in the hedge bottoms. Look out for hares, partridges and lapwings in the open fields, while in central parts around Nunburnholme you may well spot red kites with their distinctive forked tails soaring overhead.

The hawthorn hedgerows that accompany the Yorkshire Wolds Way for so many miles have their own special inhabitants. All of the common small birds are present throughout the year, as well as family groups of long-tailed tits and the occasional raiding sparrowhawk.

The beech woodland sections are often fragrant with honeysuckle, while forget-me-nots, red campions, bluebells and primroses carpet the floor in season. Where the footpath joins a metalled lane, the banks are piled with cow parsley in summer. The woodland and some hedge banks also contain a variety of mushrooms and fungi in late summer and autumn, but be warned that most of them are poisonous and the best advice is, unless you know the subject, leave them alone!

The North Sea coast near Filey

Where the trail arrives at the North Sea coast, the dramatic sea cliffs which extend southwards from Filey towards Flamborough Head provide a superb nesting site for numerous seabirds. Try to allow time to visit the famous RSPB Reserve at Bempton Cliffs just to the east of Filey (see page 120). Bempton is home to more than 200,000 seabirds during the breeding season. Species to look out for include puffin, gannet, kittiwake, razorbill and guillemot. The site and the cliffs here are well worth a visit, though, at any time of year. Migrating species passing through in spring include wheatears and a range of warblers, while

The delightful puffin is a regular visitor to Bempton Cliffs between April and July.

autumn arrivals are dominated by the thrushes, redwings, fieldfares, more warblers, stonechats and goldcrests. Short-eared owls hunt for voles here in winter. You may be able to spot a porpoise swimming in calm waters in springtime, while further offshore minki whales have been sighted. Roe deer can also be seen on the reserve.

The Yorkshire Wildlife Trust has launched a nature tourism project called the Yorkshire Nature Triangle to help promote and support the wonderful variety of wildlife found in East Yorkshire, from the Wolds to the coast, including the waterways and wetlands. For further information on their excellent nature reserves, top tips on how to spot wildlife and a listing of 'wildlife friendly' accommodation using the new accreditation the 'Puffin Mark', visit their excellent new website www.yorkshirenaturetriangle.com.

David Hockney with his painting The Arrival of Spring in Woldgate, East Yorkshire.

Art, literature and the Yorkshire Wolds

Artists

The peace and tranquillity of the Yorkshire Wolds, combined with its remoteness and beautiful dry valleys, have created a special landscape much loved by artists. However, it has been the impact of one in particular, **David Hockney**, that has brought the wonders of the Yorkshire Wolds to a much wider audience. You can read more about Hockney and his work on page 78. There is also a circular walk from the village of Warter which passes the locations of some of his most famous paintings (see page 80).

Many other artists have established small galleries in the Yorkshire Wolds. These include the wildlife artist and sculptor Robert Fuller, who has created a superb gallery in Fotherdale Farm, just off the trail near Thixendale (see page 92). Artists Ian and Stef Mitchell also draw inspiration from the Yorkshire Wolds; their studio is located near Sledmere, 3 miles (5 km) from the Yorkshire Wolds Way.

Just off the trail near Staxton Wold RAF Station is the Yorkshire Wolds Gallery, a showcase for local artists with regular exhibitions and a tea room/coffee shop (see page 124).

The Yorkshire Wolds Way National Trail has become a work of art in its own right with the establishment of 'Wander – Art on the Yorkshire Wolds Way'. This project, organised by Visit Hull and East Yorkshire (see page 138), consists of a series of specially commissioned works of art, making it the first National Trail in the country to have a project of this scale. There are six beautifully designed and thoughtfully positioned new benches along the trail, complete with stirring verse by the Scarborough poet John Wedgwood Clarke. Other works of art include the dramatic *Enclosure Rites* installation near Knapton Brow (see page 110); the unusual new bus shelter at Fridaythorpe (see page 90); and *Time and Flow*, the swirling design by artist Chris Drury, wonderfully located in a dry valley near Thixendale (see page 92).

Winifred Holtby

Writers

Winifred Holtby, the writer and journalist, was born in the village of Rudston In the Yorkshire Wolds. Her most famous novel, which was published posthumously, was *South Riding*. The book depicted life in a Yorkshire community during the 1930s and covered issues ranging from class and sexism to prejudice within local government in the build-up to the Second World War. Her first published book, *Anderby Wold*, was based on the struggles of a farming community in the Wolds during a period of social change. In addition, she wrote a critique of Virginia Woolf and was an ardent feminist, pacifist and socialist. She died in 1935, aged just 37, and is buried in All Saints churchyard in Rudston.

Although not strictly from the Wolds, the famous poet **Philip Larkin** made Hull his home for many years. You can read more about Larkin and his Yorkshire connections on page 48. You will also find a walk in Hull based on part of the Larkin Trail on page 50.

The poet Philip Larkin enjoyed cycling to villages around the Humber Estuary.

Planning your walk

An ideal introduction to long-distance walking

When planning your walk it is worth bearing in mind that the Yorkshire Wolds Way is not one of the 'heavyweights' of long-distance walking in Britain and even someone new to walking should accomplish it with ease. This makes it the ideal trail to introduce less experienced walkers to the challenge of tackling a longer route. At no point is the terrain difficult; indeed, with the exception of about half a dozen short, sharp inclines where the path climbs out of chalk dales on to the airy Wolds, the whole of the route is on level valley bottoms or open fields.

It is also a really attractive proposition to the walker who wants to escape the crowds, as the countryside of the Yorkshire Wolds is quiet and you will encounter fewer walkers than on most other National Trails.

Once you have decided to tackle the Yorkshire Wolds Way there are only a couple of things to consider.

Direction of travel

If taking on the whole 79-mile (127-km) walk, you need to decide in which direction to go. There is no reason why you should not begin on the cliffs at Filey and walk south towards the Humber Bridge. But there are some good reasons for beginning at the Humber and ending on the east coast. One is that it is usually better to walk with the sun on your back, especially on bright days when walking towards it can be dazzling. Another south–north justification is to do with the landscape itself. From its inauspicious beginnings on a muddy Humber bank, the beauty of the scenery intensifies by the day. Filey Brigg is a fine place to finish your 'Walk on the Wolds', but it is highly recommended that you extend your journey along the magnificent chalk cliffs of Bempton and Flamborough and on to Bridlington, thus completing an 'arc of chalk scenery' that is second to none in England. This book therefore describes the route from south to north.

In spite of modern agricultural improvements, wild poppies still find a foothold in many Wolds fields and hedges.

Time of year

It can be a gamble with the British weather at any time, but the east is generally speaking the drier side of the country, while late spring and early autumn can often have dry, settled weather. The best times of year to do the walk are probably in the spring, summer or autumn. All these seasons have their own special magic on the Wolds, and the chalk grassland comes alive with flowers and insects during the summer months. Winter, apart from being scenically rather dull, has the added disadvantage of fewer accommodation options, as many bed and breakfast guesthouses operate only from Easter to October, and public transport can be even harder to find. Additionally, some of the villages in the central Wolds, like Thixendale and Huggate, are notorious for being cut off by snow during the worst of the winter weather.

General information

It is recommended that you leave your car at home if planning to walk the whole route, as both ends are served by public transport and a bus links Filey to Hull. If coming from Europe to Hull by ferry, a bus will take you from the port to Hull Paragon Station where you can get a train to Hessle.

The route is described in six chapters, each one terminating in a town or village where accommodation, refreshment and public transport (except at Millington or Thixendale) can be found. Accommodation and public transport options are limited in the central part of the route, which can make planning difficult. As a result, some of the sections are quite long, especially for the inexperienced walker. Section 5, from Thixendale to Sherburn, covers 19 miles (30 km), but can be reduced in length with an overnight stop in North Grimston (see page 106) or in the Malton area (see page 108).

Circular walks

If you don't want to take on the full route, there are some wonderful circular walks on the excellent Yorkshire Wolds Way website (see page 138) which will

give you a flavour of the Wolds. This book also describes four very different walks, on pages 50, 80, 130 and 134. Another excellent source of circular walks in the Yorkshire Wolds is the Walking the Riding website: www.walkingtheriding.co.uk.

Waymarking

Because of the great need to keep to paths on agricultural land, the footpath is well signposted, especially at junctions with other rights of way and at roads. The signposts are clearly marked 'Yorkshire Wolds Way' or 'Wolds Way' and bear Natural England's National Trail symbol, a stylised acorn (🌰). The acorn is used in other places where confirmation of the correct path is required. In the southern part of the route, a larger carved acorn has been installed at 5-mile (8-km) intervals. These acorns are due be introduced along the northern part of the route when funding allows.

The old lifeboat station at Coble Landing, Filey. The lifeboat is towed to and from the sea by tractor.

Reporting a problem

If you come across a problem, ranging from a damaged gate or signpost to a ploughed-up or blocked section of path, whilst walking the trail, please report it to the East Riding of Yorkshire Council for the section between Hessle and Fridaythorpe or to North Yorkshire Council for the remainder. For more general comments and enquiries about the trail, please contact the National Trail Team (see page 138).

Easy access

To make the trail easier to use, the National Trail team is carrying out a programme of replacing stiles with kissing-gates. You may still encounter the occasional stile on the northern part of the route, but these will be replaced with gates when funding allows. There are some easy-access circular walks listed on the Yorkshire Wolds Way website (see page 138).

Postcards, completion cards and Tracker packs

So that you can tell all your friends about the walk, the Yorkshire Wolds Way National Trail team have produced a series of seven free postcards which can be picked up at Tourist Information Centres along the route (see page 138), and a special 'I've completed the Yorkshire Wolds Way' postcard is available at both ends of the trail. To give families a fun introduction to the Yorkshire Wolds Way, special Tracker packs are available at £5 per day to hire from Tourist Information Centres along the way. These packs are loaded with information and activities for children and are based on short walks at Welton, Londesborough, Wharram Percy and Filey.

Other trails that link to the Yorkshire Wolds Way

From south to north as follows:

Viking Way
This route starts in Rutland and passes through Leicestershire and Lincolnshire for 147 miles (237 km) to end at Barton upon Humber on the southern side of the Humber Bridge.

Trans Pennine Trail
Britain's first long-distance multi-use trail runs 215 miles (346 km) from Hornsea on the east coast to Southport on Merseyside.

Beverley 20
This trail is 20 miles (32 km) long, starting at the Humber Bridge and finishing at Beverley Minster.

High Hunsley Circuit
A 24-mile (39-km) circuit starting and finishing at the village of Walkington, passing close to Welton, Brantingham, North Newbald and South Cave.

Hudson Way
Named after George Hudson, the 'Railway King', who lived at Londesborough, this 11-mile (17.5-km) flat route runs along the disused railway track between Beverley and Market Weighton.

Wilberforce Way
A 60-mile (97-km) linear route established to commemorate the bicentenary of the abolition of slavery. It connects Hull, Pocklington and York – all places that played important roles in the life of Sir William Wilberforce.

Minster Way
This 50-mile (80-km) route links the two famous minsters of York and Beverley.

Chalkland Way
A 40-mile (64-km) circuit starting and finishing in Pocklington, passing through Thixendale.

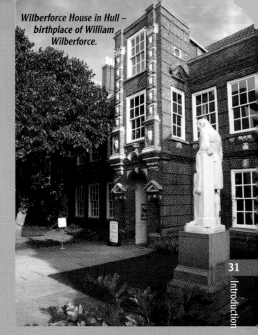

Wilberforce House in Hull – birthplace of William Wilberforce.

Pilgrimage of Grace Heritage Walk
An 8¼-mile (13.2-km) linear route linking Pocklington and Warter via Kilnwick Percy and Nunburnholme. It follows the route of the great Tudor rebellion of 1536.

Centenary Way
This long route was devised to commemorate 100 years of Yorkshire County Council. It runs for 83 miles (134 km) from York to Filey Brigg.

Headland Way
A 12-mile (19-km) route from Black Cliff Nab, Speeton to Sewerby Steps, past Bempton Cliffs and around the promontory of Flamborough Head.

Cleveland Way National Trail
This long-distance trail starts in the picturesque town of Helmsley and crosses the North York Moors to meet the coast at Saltburn. It then heads down the coast to meet the Yorkshire Wolds Way at Filey Brigg. It is 109 miles (175 km) in length. For full details on this magnificent trail, visit www.nationaltrail.co.uk/clevelandway. An official National Trail Guide to the Cleveland Way is published by Aurum Press in the same series as this book.

The marker for the start of the Yorkshire Wolds Way at Hessle Haven.

PART TWO
Yorkshire Wolds Way

via North Ferriby and Welton

13 miles (21 km)

Ascent 1,221 feet (372 metres)
Descent 1,058 feet (322 metres)
Highest point Brantingham Wold 464 feet (141 metres)
Lowest point Humber Foreshore 0 feet (0 metres)

A fascinating and varied section making this a great introduction to the Yorkshire Wolds Way. You are transported gently from the mighty Humber Estuary into typical Yorkshire Wold scenery, where you can experience the first of many wonderful dales to come. To add to the variety, you will also pass close to a couple of interesting small villages with attractive churches. In order to avoid a short alternative route away from the Humber, it is best to check on tide times when planning your walk (see page 138).

Things to look out for

▌**York** This wonderful medieval city, located about 20 miles (32 km) to the west of the Yorkshire Wolds Way, is the main gateway to the East Riding. The city has a long and interesting history. It was known as Eboracum by the Romans, Eoforwic by the Saxons and Jorvik by the Vikings. Edward IV is reputed to have said that 'The history of York is the history of England.'

The city is dominated by its Gothic minster, one of the most magnificent cathedrals in the country. It has been rebuilt since the devastating fire of 1984 and the East Window has probably the largest area of stained glass in the world. The city's narrow cobbled back streets and alleyways,

known as 'snickelways' and 'ginnels', including The Shambles, still retain a medieval feel and are fascinating to explore. York still has many of its old city walls and there are plenty of walking routes to choose from to explore this attractive historic place.

York, with its excellent transport connections to East Yorkshire, also has many 'wet weather attractions', including a superb range of museums: the Jorvik Centre, the Castle Museum, the Yorkshire Museum and the famous National Railway Museum. The latest visitor attraction tells the story of York's chocolate heritage! For further information on visiting York, please contact York Visitor Information Centre (see page 139).

Kingston upon Hull A major city on the banks of the River Humber, Kingston upon Hull has a long maritime history dating back to the days of the Hanseatic League. It developed steadily as a trading port and the first of many docks was opened in 1778. The early 19th century saw a boom in whaling and the city further grew as a result of new railway links in the 1840s. It was heavily bombed during the Second World War but much of the historic city has been rebuilt.

After a period of post-war industrial decline, the city embarked on a series of successful regeneration projects to redevelop rundown areas and bring a new vitality to Hull. One of these is The Deep, a stunning new aquarium and visitor centre with over 3,500 fish. Built on derelict dockland, it is described as the world's only submarium, with Europe's deepest viewing tunnel.

Despite much redevelopment, Hull retains a superb Old Town area around the Holy Trinity Church. This is one of the largest churches in the country and the magnificent tower rises proudly over the surrounding area. Nearby is the Museums Quarter, which consists of four fascinating museums covering the long and varied history of the city.

Hull is rightly famous for its associations with the poet Philip Larkin. The recently launched Larkin Trail has turned the city into a literary destination. For further information about Philip Larkin, the Larkin Trail and details of a walk along part of it, see pages 48–53.

In addition, three other imaginative walking trails have been established around the centre of Hull, reflecting its maritime, industrial and cultural history:

Seven Seas Fish Trail Along this popular circular route you can seek out the 41 fish sculptures around the banks of the Hull and Humber Rivers in the heart of the maritime city.

Walking with Wilberforce Heritage Trail There are historic links with slavery here, as William Wilberforce the abolitionist was born in Hull. This route links landmarks from his life around the old city. There is also a long-distance trail called the Wilberforce Way which connects Hull to Pocklington and York (see 'Other trails', page 31).

Looking back towards the enormous span of the Humber Bridge on the first stage of the journey.

The disused Victorian lighthouse which stands at the southern tip of Spurn Point may become a heritage centre for this fascinating area.

Victoria Dock Heritage Trail This self-guided walk takes visitors around the 19th-century industrial heritage of the dock just east of the Fish Trail.

For further details on Hull itself and free walking trails leaflets, contact the Hull Tourist Information Centre (page 138).

■ **Holderness** If you have time, it is well worth exploring the peninsula of land to the south-east of Hull known as Holderness. It is a fascinating, remote area with an 'end of the world' feel. It is home to one of the best parish churches in the country (see Patrington below), an inland lighthouse and a unique sand spit known as Spurn Head – see below.

■ **Patrington** This small village is unremarkable except for its truly magnificent church. Known as the 'Queen of Holderness', the parish church of St Patrick is one of the most beautiful in the country and a classic example of the early 14th-century Decorated style of Gothic. It is wonderfully proportioned, with some superb stone carvings and possesses a full set of Easter Sepulchre,

complete with sleeping soldiers and an image of Christ with angels. On the wall of the church car park can be found a plaque from the Larkin Trail.

■ **Withernsea** This quirky seaside resort on the east coast used to boast a pier but, having been hit by so many vessels, it was eventually removed. The elaborate castle-like entrance to the beach is all that remains of the pier as a testament to a bygone era. The lighthouse, 127 feet (39 metres) high, dominates the town as it looms incongruously from its unusual inland location. It is no longer in use and now houses a fascinating museum (open Easter–October).

An interesting and unusual place to visit near Withernsea is the RAF base at Holmpton, where you can enjoy a tour of the Cold War underground bunkers.

■ **Spurn Point National Nature Reserve** Also known as Spurn Head, this is one of the most unusual coastal features in the country. It is a long, narrow sand spit which stretches across the Humber Estuary for 3½ miles (5.6 km) and is barely 50 yards (60 metres) wide in places. It was formed by a process of erosion and deposition under the effects of long-shore drift and is constantly changing shape. Made of a series of shingle and sandbanks held together by marram grass and sea buckthorn, it is a fragile environment, extremely vulnerable to North Sea storm damage. Every 250 years or so the spit is breached and the process of growth starts again. Owned by the Yorkshire Wildlife Trust, it is a wonderful location for migrating birds. Other wildlife include roe deer, foxes and hares, as well as marine species such as porpoises and seals. Common lizards, a huge range of insects, butterflies, moths and a wide variety of plant species can also be found here in season.

There is an excellent circular walk of about 1 mile (1.6 km) from the car park, which allows visitors to appreciate fully that 'back of beyond' feeling that Spurn evokes. See the excellent Walk the Riding website www.walkingtheriding.co.uk for further details of this walk and others.

Look out for the Philip Larkin plaque on the battery wall by the car park which marks the very end of the Larkin Trail.

1 Hessle At the start of the Yorkshire Wolds Way walk, Hessle is part of the Greater Hull area but a separate town in its own right. Recent industries have included shipbuilding and chalk-quarrying. The town suffered badly in the floods of 2007, which caused much damage and one fatality. An annual festivity which has been carried on since the early 1800s is a large community event known as the Hessle Feast.

A plaque from the Larkin Trail can be seen on a wall outside a private residence on the main Hull Road.

2 Humber Estuary Often referred to, erroneously, as the 'River' Humber, this mighty estuary is formed by the confluence of the Rivers Trent and Yorkshire Ouse, which between them drain 9,650 square miles (25,000 square km), equivalent to one fifth of England's land surface.

The estuary was created more than 70 million years ago when the chalk beds, composed of millions of tiny marine organisms, were thrust to the surface by movement of the earth's crust, and the water that had covered them drained through several massive channels to form new seas. One of the biggest channels was the Humber, leaving what became the Lincolnshire Wolds on the south bank and the Yorkshire Wolds on the north. Originally it drained into the North Sea on the eastern fringe of Hull, but the last Ice Age dumped huge amounts of boulder clay to form what today is Holderness – a vast flat area running from Hull to the chalk headland at Flamborough.

Through the mouth of the Humber the first settlers arrived from the Continent. Simple Bronze Age boats hollowed out from oak trees by fire and crude tools have been found (see North Ferriby below). It was also by the Humber that the invaders who were to make the earliest impact on the Wolds, the Parisii, arrived from France c.300 BC. They cultivated the landscape and left traces that can still be seen as earthworks near Huggate and Millington, as well as a number of chariot burials of chieftains. Romans and Vikings used the Humber during their invasions; it was the northern frontier of the Roman Empire at one time. Also it was from Immingham Creek, on the south bank, that the earliest Pilgrim Fathers sailed in 1608.

The last Humber sloop: Amy Howson.

Since the Industrial Revolution, the Humber has been one of the most important shipping lanes in Europe, with navigation schemes connecting the port of Hull with the great inland cities of Sheffield, Nottingham and Leeds, and, via the Leeds–Liverpool Canal, with the west coast. Cargo vessels still navigate the gritty brown waters, but the channels and sandbanks are dynamic and have been changing for thousands of years. The shipping lanes have to be regularly altered and river mariners treat the Humber with great respect.

3 Humber Bridge and 4 Country Park The Humber Bridge is one of the most spectacular man-made structures encountered on a National Trail in Britain. End to end, from the cliffs above the Hessle foreshore to the outskirts of Barton-upon-Humber on the south bank, it stretches 7,283½ feet (4,405 metres), or just under 1½ miles (2.4 km) long. Its most important dimension is the single span between the two giant piers: 4,626 feet (1,410 metres), which made it the world's longest single-span suspension bridge for 16 years. Toll-paying traffic on dual two-lane carriageways and two

pedestrian/cycle paths pass some 150 feet (46 metres) above the estuary. Exceptionally keen walkers can arrive at the start of the Yorkshire Wolds Way via the Viking Way long-distance footpath, which begins at Oakham in Leicestershire and ends 140 miles (225 km) north on the other side of the Humber Bridge.

A regular ferry crossing of the Humber was established in 1825 and operated between Hull Corporation Pier and New Holland until just before the bridge was opened by the Queen on 17 July 1981. Plans for a railway tunnel in the 1870s and a road bridge in the 1930s collapsed through lack of funds, and the present structure, which cost more than £90 million to build, has since run up debts many times that amount in interest charges. Its construction was considered essential to the creation of the new county of Humberside in 1974, formed from the old East Riding and part of north Lincolnshire.

To the immediate west of the north bank pier is the Humber Bridge Country Park, a 48-acre (19-hectare) site containing meadows, woodlands, ponds, cliffs, an old mill, nature trails, information centre, café and toilets. The park was formed from the remains of an old chalk quarry, first worked in 1317. Access is immediately off the Yorkshire Wolds Way by clearly signed footpaths leading away from the shore.

Look out for the Philip Larkin plaque on the north tower of the Humber Bridge.

5 North Ferriby Known to locals simply as Ferriby, this village on the north bank of the Humber once boasted a magnificent 12th-century priory, and the attractive church is well worth a visit. Today, however, North Ferriby is famous for a discovery made along the riverside by two brothers in 1937. They spotted some wood protruding from the mud and further exploration led to the uncovering of the remains of three Bronze Age boats, constructed from bevelled oak planks and moss caulking bound with yew withies. One of the brothers made more finds along the river bank during the 1940s and 1960s. Recent research funded by English Heritage dates one of these vessels back nearly 4,000 years, placing it amongst the oldest of its kind yet discovered in western Europe. Now regarded as one of the most significant archaeological finds in Britain, these 50-foot (16-metre)-long vessels would have been paddled by up to 18 oarsmen, possibly assisted by a sail. Originally thought to have been used as Humber ferry boats, it is now apparent that they would also have been used for sea-going trade.

7 Welton Now an expensive dormitory for Hull commuters, the village of Welton is not only one of the most charming to be found along the Yorkshire Wolds Way but also has perhaps the greatest claim to fame. It was here in 1739 that the legendary highwayman Dick Turpin, scourge of all coach travellers between London and York, was arrested. The full story of how he came to be in this seemingly peaceful village can be learned in the Green Dragon Inn, Cowgate, which is as good an excuse to take refreshment as you will ever get. A copy of his record of arrest, to be found inside the pub, says that one John Palmer had stolen some horses in Lincolnshire and driven them across the Humber to sell them. He got drunk at the Green Dragon, shot a gamecock and was subsequently unmasked as the famous Turpin. He was tried at York Assizes and sent to the gallows.

9 Brantingham This village lies on the south-western fringes of the Yorkshire Wolds. The most impressive building is Brantingham Hall, a 2½-storey red-brick house overlooking the village pond. Further south is a Gothic war memorial, built from an assortment of features from Hull's Victorian Town Hall (replaced in 1914 by the Guildhall) and described by one expert as 'lovably awful'.

All Saints, Brantingham, nestling snugly in its wooded dale, has the most picturesque setting of any church encountered along the Yorkshire Wolds Way, with the possible exception of the ruined St Martin's at Wharram Percy. Bits of it can be dated to the 13th century, but most of what you see today can be attributed to a restoration by G. E. Street, paid for by the wealthy Sykes family of Sledmere. Brantingham has a fine pub, the Triton Arms, named after an ancient god of the sea from Greek mythology, reflecting the maritime links of the Sykes family. The only other pub in the country called the Triton Arms is at the Sykes estate village of Sledmere (see page 100). Just to the south-east of the village a large Roman villa was discovered in 1941.

Walking the Yorkshire Wolds Way on a crisp winter's day. Brantingham Church lies in the valley below.

Route description

Given the overall dominance of the Humber Bridge, it may appear a little odd that the official start of the National Trail is at Hessle Haven, about ½ mile (800 metres) to the east. The reasons for this are linked to the establishment of the route in the early 1980s. Whether you arrive in **Hessle 1** by train or bus, it is only a short walk to the start of the Yorkshire Wolds Way on Livingstone Way opposite the old Ferryboat Inn **A** (currently the San Luca wine bar and restaurant).

On the opposite bank of Hessle Haven was the site of one of the last yards on the Humber, where locally distinctive keel boats were built in the early part of the last century. Turn down a surfaced path opposite known as Jeans Walk and follow it towards the river and then right along the bank of the **Humber Estuary 2**, with magnificent views of the **Humber**

Bridge **3** ahead. Just before the bridge you will pass the stone sculpture **B** which marks a more photogenic start to your walk to the North Sea (the brother of which you will eventually meet on Filey Brigg). The white pebbles and boulders along the river bank are a sure sign that the chalk Wolds are not far away.

The area around the bridge contains a Tourist Information Centre, many car parking spaces and visitor facilities, including information boards explaining the Humber's history and wildlife. Keep ahead on Cliff Road and once under the giant legs (510 feet/156 metres high, with foundations 26 feet/8 metres deep) you will see the frontage of the **Humber Bridge Country Park 4** with useful facilities, including toilets, and the ruin of an old five-sail windmill. The park was established around a chalk quarry and opened in 1986.

Hessle to South Cave

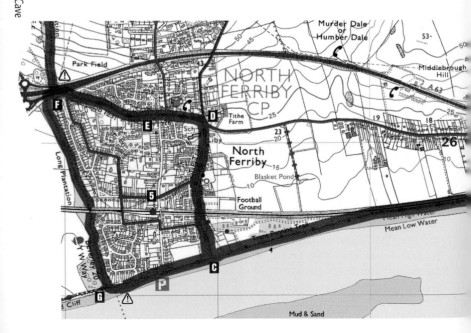

Look for the sign and the short flight of steps on the left which gives access to the shore to pass in front of 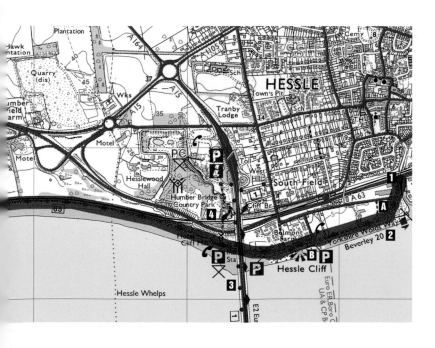 the Country Park Inn. The route then joins a wide track bordered by the Hull–York railway line (opened in 1840) on the right. Keep an eye out for cyclists, as you are sharing this route with the Trans Pennine Trail, Britain's first long-distance multi-use trail (see page 31).

When you reach the reed pond **C**, care should be taken when there is a high tide or if the river is in spate, as the path along the shore may be dangerous. For further details on the tide times, see page 138. If the tide is high or you are in any doubt, turn right on the alternative route, then go straight ahead on reaching the tarmac road, under the railway bridge, past the church, then left **D** along North Ferriby High Street **E**, which leads into Melton Road. Keep on this road to rejoin the Way at the main A63 trunk road crossing **F**.

If the shore is clear, however, continue ahead down the steps to the shoreline and keep going until you reach the point where the trees meet the river **G**. It was near here that important Bronze Age discoveries were made in the 1930s.

Go up the metal steps and follow the wide path into the appropriately named Long Plantation. This is a peaceful, pleasant walk through woodland and a real contrast to the estuary section. Cross the railway line on a bridge with wooden slats. You will emerge eventually on to the main road **F**.

⬛ ⇄ ⬛ *Turn right here for the shops, services and railway station of* **North Ferriby 5**.

Turn left here to cross the bridge over the A63 – great care is needed when crossing the slip roads here. On the far side turn right and then left to rejoin the

Dusk arrives over the Humber Bridge, one of the world's longest single-span bridges.

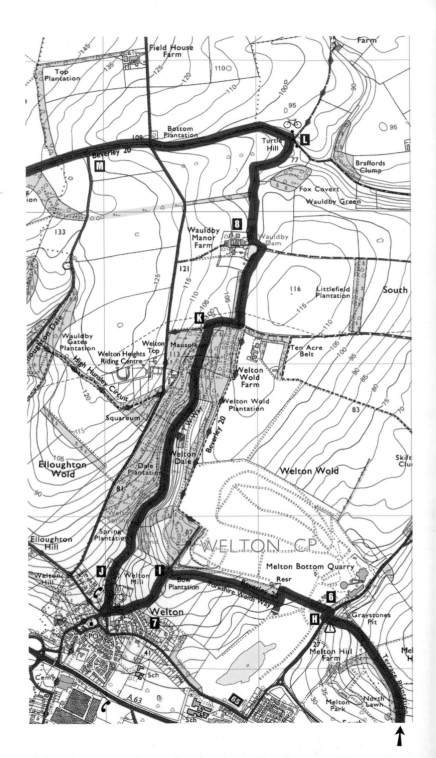

route through the trees of Terrace Plantation. Here begins your first long gentle climb.

Pass through the grounds of the North Hull Scout Group campsite. Go through a wooden kissing-gate and cross the metalled road with care , then follow the track past the huge chasm of Melton Bottom Quarry . Look out for a left turn into Bow Plantation, an enclosed path that runs parallel to the track through woodland with occasional views over the Humber Estuary. Turn left down the road which descends to the village of **Welton** , your earliest experience of a Wolds village. It also happens to be one of the prettiest, especially around St Helen's Church and the mill stream.

To visit the Green Dragon pub and the village of Welton, simply keep ahead.

The Yorkshire Wolds Way continues to the right up Dale Road to one of the many secluded stretches of the footpath. Pass the modern houses Welton Lodge and Welton Mill, then continue beyond

Dale Cottage to Welton Dale. This is lined with trees and is a wonderful path, with the added advantage of being a gorgeous sun-trap in summer. A large kissing-gate gives access to Welton Wold Plantation, through which, up to the left, you may catch a glimpse of the domed mausoleum (no public access) built in 1818 by the erstwhile occupants of Welton House, the Raikes family.

Go through a wooden kissing-gate to cross the concrete road and turn right inside the field edge, then after a short distance turn left through a gap. At the end of the conifer plantation you will have a good view of the impressive Wauldby Manor Farm and as you approach Wauldby Dam you may also spot the little church amongst the trees. Turn left then sharp right by the farm cottages and walk on a gently undulating track until you reach a junction, where you turn left . The high hawthorn hedges hereabouts are some of the most impressive in the area. At the road junction go straight ahead and, where the road turns sharp left , continue ahead along the broad track

bridleway section of the trail between Wauldby Manor Farm and Brantingham.

past Long Plantation. The track merges into a tarmac lane from which there are impressive views over flat terrain towards the industrial towns of South and West Yorkshire. As you descend the steep lane, look out for an enclosed path on the right **N** which drops down towards Brantingham Church.

🍴 🚌 *To visit the Triton Inn and the beautiful village of* **Brantingham 9***, continue down the road and turn left.*

Turn right up the road past All Saints Church, Brantingham **10**, in its picturesque setting and at the first sweeping bend **O** turn left to follow a narrow path through a wooden kissing-gate into the forest. At the top of the hill

drop down towards Woodale Farm **11**, turning right just before the buildings. In a short distance branch off to the left through a wooden kissing-gate and climb uphill to reach Mount Airy Farm **12**. Immediately past the farm buildings turn sharp left and follow the tarmac road down to join the road **P**, with lovely views beyond South Cave as you descend.

🍴 🚌 *Turn left at the road, leaving the trail, and keep ahead for ½ mile (800 metres) to reach South Cave. This is mostly a dormitory for affluent Hull commuters, but it also has good accommodation and a couple of eating places, making it a handy overnight stop for Yorkshire Wolds Way walkers.*

Hessle to South Cave

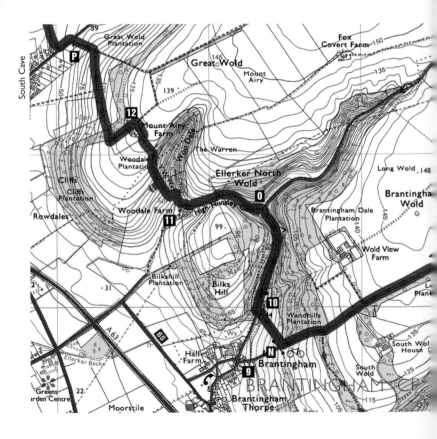

Brantingham Church, centrepiece of a popular and picturesque dale.

Public transport

Hull (3 miles/4.8 km) ≋ 🚌 ⛴
Hessle (on route) ≋ 🚌
North Ferriby (½ mile/800 m) ≋ 🚌
Welton (on route) 🚌
Brough (1½ miles/2.4 km) ≋ 🚌
Elloughton (1½ miles/2.4 km) 🚌
Brantingham (¼ mile/400 m) 🚌
South Cave (½ mile/800 m) 🚌
Taxis/minicabs: Hull Hessle North Ferriby Brough

Refreshments and toilets

Hull (3 miles/4.8 km) 🍺 ☕ wide selection
Hessle (on route) 🍺 Country Park Inn, Marquis of Granby, Brewers Fayre (Premier Inn)
North Ferriby (½ mile/800 m) 🍺 Duke of Cumberland

Welton (on route) 🍺 Green Dragon
Brough (1½ miles/2.4 km) 🍺 Ferry Inn, Red Hawk, Cross Keys
Elloughton (1½ miles/2.4 km) 🍺 Half Moon
Brantingham (¼ mile/400 m) 🍺 Triton Inn
South Cave (½ mile/800 m) 🍺 Bear Inn ☕ Gallery Café
Food shops: Hull, Hessle, North Ferriby
Public toilets: Hull, Hessle (Country Park)

Accommodation

Hull (3 miles/4.8 km) wide range
Hessle (on route) Redcliffe House (B&B), Premier Inn Hull West, Country Park Inn
North Ferriby (½ mile/800 m) Hallmark Hotel
Brantingham (¼ mile/400 m) Keepers Lodge (B&B, camping)
South Cave (½ mile/800 m) Rudstone Walk (B&B), Silver Trees (B&B), Cave Castle Hotel

Philip Larkin

Confirmed since his death in 1985 as Britain's greatest post-war poet, Philip Larkin spent 30 years living and working in Hull, and it was here that he wrote his finest poetry. Born in Coventry in 1922, he read English Language and Literature at St John's College, Oxford, before taking

Plaque marking the end of the Larkin Trail.

up a lifelong career as a librarian, in Shropshire, Leicester (where he met Kingsley Amis, whom he subsequently inspired to write his most famous novel, *Lucky Jim*) and Belfast before being appointed University Librarian at the Brynmor Jones Library at the University of Hull in 1955. Larkin was largely responsible for building it into one of the most distinguished university libraries in the country, and he remained there till his death.

His first book of poetry, *The North Ship*, appeared in 1945, closely followed by two novels, *Jill* and *A Girl in Winter*. But it was his second collection, *The Less Deceived*, in 1955, containing now classic poems like 'Church Going' and 'Poetry of Departures', that made his reputation – a standing enhanced by *The Whitsun Weddings* in 1964, whose magnificent title poem has become the most famous of all Larkin's works. It was then ten years until his final volume, *High Windows*, its more sombre tone symptomatic of Larkin's increasing difficulty in writing, and 'Aubade', his last long poem which appeared in 1977, is bleak with intimations of mortality.

Pensive and jaunty by turns, Larkin's poetry is notable for its narrative quality – 'Church

The superb sculpture of the poet Philip Larkin which greets arrivals at Hull Paragon Station.

Going' describes his visit to a deserted country church, 'The Whitsun Weddings' a bank holiday train journey from Hull to London as newly-married couples board at every station to go on their honeymoons – for its peerless control of poetic form in stanza, metre and rhyme scheme, and for its ability to articulate profound philosophical musings in language that is always both comprehensible and memorable. 'Annus Mirabilis', with its famous line about sexual intercourse only beginning in 1963, 'which was rather late for me', is an example of his self-deprecating and often baleful wit; 'An Arundel Tomb' illustrates Larkin's compassion and wistful, elegiac side.

A retiring man who never sought the limelight, he declined an OBE in 1968, but did accept the Companion of Honour, and in 1984 after the death of Sir John Betjeman he refused the position of Poet Laureate. Hull's 'adopted son', Larkin lived for 18 years in the Pearson Park area of the city before moving to Newland Park near the university in 1974. Larkin died in 1985, aged 63, and is buried in Cottingham Cemetery and commemorated by a statue at Paragon Station.

A Larkin Trail, taking in 25 signed locations in and around the Hull area covering all the important and inspirational places in his life and poetry, was established on the 25th anniversary of his death. You can get an excellent feel for the city section of the trail by following the 'Larkin Walk' on page 50.

The remaining six plaque locations can be found further afield in the East Riding, from the village of Blacktoft up the Humber Estuary – a favourite cycling destination for Larkin – to the tip of the narrow spit of land known as Spurn Point at the end of Holderness, numinously evoked in his poem 'Here'.

Full details of the Larkin Trail can be found at www.thelarkintrail.co.uk, or visit the Hull Tourist Information Centre.

A Philip Larkin Walk

This 6-mile (9.6-km) walk from Hull Paragon Station to Cottingham Station is mostly on pavements, but there are some sections on footpaths and through urban parks. You can reduce the amount of road-walking by taking a bus from the University of Hull to Cottingham.

Before you start your walk you may wish to visit the **Royal Hotel** next door to the start of the Larkin Trail, as well as other city-centre places that the poet frequented. Taking along a copy of the detailed Larkin Trail Guide (see page 49) will give you more information about the poet and help you locate the trail plaques (shown as ★).

The walk starts beside the impressive **Philip Larkin statue** that stands behind platforms 3 and 4 at Hull Paragon Station. The statue is the work of the sculptor Martin Jennings, who also produced the Sir John Betjeman statue at London's St Pancras Station. In the station, also look out for the five slate plaques featuring Larkin's work and the special round teak bench in his honour.

Face the statue with the platforms behind you and turn right to leave the station, following signs for the Anlaby Road exit. A quick right then a left turn brings you on to the busy Anlaby Road. Pause to admire the superb old building opposite, which is now a pub but was once the **Regent Cinema**, and the equally magnificent **Old Tower Cinema** next to the station.

Turn right down Anlaby Road, with huge but colourful tower blocks opposite. To your right you will soon notice the vast square bulk of the **Hull Royal Infirmary** building to which Larkin was a regular visitor. He referred to the hospital as 'The lucent comb' in his poem 'The Building'. At the traffic lights turn right into Argyle Street, passing

the side of the hospital with its old Victorian buildings behind. As you cross the railway you can see the new KC Stadium, home to Hull City Football Club, over to your left. At the end of the road, now called Derringham Street, turn left into Spring Bank and then immediately right into Princes Avenue.

To visit the incredible **Hull General Cemetery**, which was much loved by Philip Larkin, keep ahead at the junction into Spring Bank West, where the cemetery can be found on your right – a quiet green oasis in the heart of the city. It was privately run until 1972, when it closed for burials and maintenance was passed to the City Council.

Continue past the attractive shops of Princes Avenue and the streets on the left named after famous Nottinghamshire estates until **Pearson Park** appears to your right. Our walk goes into the park, but if you want to see the former **Nuffield Hospital** where Larkin spent his last days, turn left into Westbourne Avenue and walk to the junction with Salisbury Road. The hospital building is on your left by the attractive roundabout with an old drinking fountain.

Take a short right and left to follow the minor road into the park, which is the oldest public park in the city. It was given to the City of Hull in 1860 by the Lord Mayor Zachariah Charles Pearson and is a great place to explore. Look out for the Victorian conservatory (open daily in spring and summer) with its surprising tropical vegetation and resident iguana. There are also statues to Queen Victoria and Prince Albert. The park has a café (opening times are weather dependent) and public toilets. Larkin, who lived for 18 years in the attic flat of **32 Pearson Park**, one of the mansions overlooking the park, moved away only because the university sold the building. It was here that he wrote his most famous poems from the 'High Windows' of the attic flat.

Follow the minor road through the park, but by the children's playground take a path to the left which takes you back to Princes Avenue. Turn right and cross the road at the second road crossing before turning left into Queens Road with **The**

Queens pub, a favourite watering hole of Larkin's, opposite. Follow the road round the right-hand bend, where it becomes Newlands Avenue. This shop-lined thoroughfare has a bustling atmosphere.

At the end of the road turn left into the busy Cottingham Road and head towards the university. On the opposite side of the road

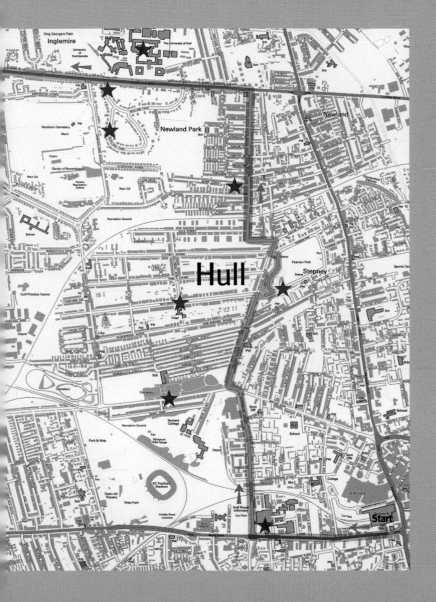

is the **Newlands** area where Larkin lived for the rest of his life after leaving his Pearson Park attic flat. There is a blue plaque outside the house, which is located at **105 Newland Park**.

You now pass the main **University of Hull** buildings on your right, with the distinctive tower block of the **Brynmor Jones Library** where Larkin worked for so many years. He referred to it as a 'Lifted Study-Storehouse' and librarianship seemed to suit his lifestyle. At the time of writing, the library was undergoing a major redevelopment.

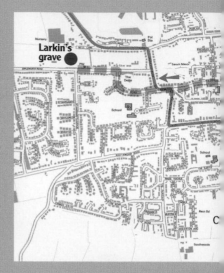

The distance from the university to Cottingham is about 2½ miles (4 km). Regular buses run along the main Cottingham Road; take no. 105 to reduce the amount of road-walking. It will drop you at The Lawns in Cottingham, which is very close to Cottingham Cemetery.

Continuing on foot, keep ahead on the Cottingham Road beyond the university until you reach a roundabout. Cross it and continue in the same direction. Just beyond Golf Links Road on your right you pass the sign that says you are leaving the City of

Hessle to South Cave

Hull and entering the East Riding of Yorkshire. This is now called the Hull Road and there is open countryside on your right. As you pass a large pub on your left-hand side, the **West Bulls Carvery** (another Larkin favourite), cross over the road and keep going in the same direction over a busy dual carriageway.

Look out for a public footpath directly opposite heading in the same direction. This path follows a track called Snuff Mill Lane, which can be muddy in parts, to enter some open countryside. Ahead lies the Hull–Scarborough railway line; cross over the tracks via two kissing-gates. Beyond the line the path narrows into a grassy area popular with dog-walkers.

Very soon you enter the housing of **Cottingham** village through concrete bollards over a minor road. Keep ahead in the same direction, crossing another road and passing through more bollards as you aim towards a large house – the **Old Snuff Mill**. Snuff was manufactured in the 18th century to the south of the village and this large house was built in 1750 for the mill-owner, William Travis.

PHILIP LARKIN
1922 - 1985
WRITER

On the map: Finish, New Village, GHAM, Woodlane Farm, The Bungalow, Loatleys, Pickhill, Wood Lane, Gengs, Clemminson Hall, Magnolia House, Nursery, School, Playing Fields, Police Training Centre, Playground, King George's, Ingle

Keep on Snuff Mill Lane to reach the main road, now called Newgate Street, and turn left then right into King Street to reach the centre of the busy village of Cottingham. With a parish population in excess of 17,000 people, Cottingham lays claim to being the largest village in England. Its heart is the **Market Green**, which holds a market every Thursday.

Just beyond the Market Green, pass the **Duke of Cumberland** pub, a 'jazz session' venue for Philip Larkin, before turning right on to Hallgate.

You will need to walk an extra mile (1.6 km) each way to visit **Cottingham Cemetery** where Larkin is buried. To do this, turn left into Hallgate, keep ahead at the mini-roundabout and take a left turn into Dene Road. Follow the road as it bends round to the right, then turn left into Eppleworth Road. Cottingham Cemetery can be found a short distance down the

road on your right. Enter by the main gate and Larkin's unassuming white grave can be found near the entrance, to your left. Retrace your steps to the village centre.

Keep ahead on Hallgate, aiming towards **St Mary's, Cottingham**, where Larkin's funeral service took place. The church dates mainly from the 14th century, with a magnificent Perpendicular-style tower which can be seen from miles around.

Just before the church head right down a narrow alleyway called Church Walk, passing the wonderful old buildings of **St Mary's Hall** and the **Church House** next door; this dates from 1729 and was originally built as a workhouse. At the end of the alleyway turn right back on to Hallgate and left up Station Road to arrive at Cottingham Station. Here you can catch a regular train on the Scarborough–Hull line back to Hull Paragon Station.

2 South Cave to Goodmanham/ Market Weighton

via East Dale and Swin Dale

To Goodmanham 11 miles (17.7 km)/to Market Weighton 12 miles (19 km)

Ascent To Goodmanham: 1,274 ft (388 m); to Market Weighton: 1,213 ft (370 m)

Descent To Goodmanham: 1,239 ft (378 m); to Market Weighton: 1,280 feet (390 m)

Highest point Both routes: Drewton Wold 533 ft (162 m)

Lowest point To Goodmanham: Springwells 139 ft (42 m); to Market Weighton: 92 ft (28 m)

This section of the Yorkshire Wolds follows classic woldland scenery for the first part but more level walking towards the end of the section. There are no facilities at all for walkers en route, although North Newbald is not far off the trail and would make an excellent lunch stop. There are also two options to consider when route-planning. You can either finish at the village of Goodmanham, which has an excellent pub but limited transport and few other facilities; or you can head along the alternative route towards Market Weighton, which is a town with a good range of shops and pubs but only limited accommodation.

Things to look out for

1 South Cave This village was almost certainly inhabited during Roman times, lying as it did on the main road from Lincoln to York, but there are no surviving relics from this period. Unusually, there are two 'ends' to the village. The West End is centred around All Saints Church, a Victorian restoration of a medieval building, and it was here that the earliest settlement was established. Charters for markets and fairs were granted in 1291 and 1314, but in the Middle Ages the market moved ½ mile (800 metres) eastwards to what is today's main village centre. The most interesting building is the Market Hall, a yellow-grey brick structure built in 1796. Up the hill is Cave Castle, a castellated Gothic house built in 1804 for the Barnards, wealthy Hull shipping merchants, but now converted into a hotel with golf club.

■ North Newbald With its classic green and two good pubs, North Newbald has the timeless atmosphere of an English village. If walking from South Cave, the short diversion makes it an excellent lunch stop. The most interesting feature of the village is its famous cruciform church of St Nicholas, said to be the finest Norman church in the East Riding. It was built around 1140 and has been exceptionally well preserved. Uniquely, the church has three Norman doorways and a Coronation clock dating from 1911.

Sancton A small village on the main A1034 road with an excellent pub/restaurant called The Star. A 6th-century pagan cremation site was discovered near here in the 1850s. Artefacts, including pottery urns and metalwork, along with human remains were discovered. Many are stored at the Ashmolean Museum in Oxford but there is also a fine display at the Hull and East Riding Museum.

5 Rifle Butts Quarry This nationally important geological reserve is managed by the Yorkshire Wildlife Trust. The quarry face shows a section of Red and White Chalk overlying Lias strata; hundreds of metres of intervening rocks are 'missing'. It is so named as it served as a rifle range until the Second World War. Over 150 species of flora have been recorded on this small nature reserve.

Only a short distance off the National Trail, North Newbald is well worth a detour for its Norman church, village green and two excellent pubs.

Route description

To rejoin the National Trail from **South Cave** 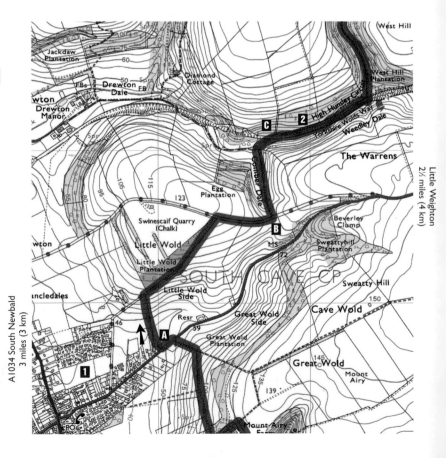, retrace your steps back up Beverley Road and just beyond the village find the path **A** on the left, which drops down to cross a small beck. This route ascends gently to Little Wold Plantation, an attractive beech and ash woodland owned by the Woodland Trust. Turn to the right and walk along the edge of the trees for about ½ mile (800 metres). This offers splendid views south across the Humber Estuary which can be appreciated from the attractive new benches installed by the National Trail team as part of the 'Wander – Art on the Yorkshire Wolds Way' scheme. When the path joins a track, turn right and descend the slope to Comber Dale, going left **B** through a large kissing-gate and down along a delightful path into one of the most serene parts of the walk. Just before the point where the path curves right into Weedley Dale is Weedley Springs, from which North Cave's stream rises.

Through the gate ahead **C** is a section of the dismantled Hull & Barnsley Railway line **2**. Cross this and follow the path running parallel to it for nearly ½ mile

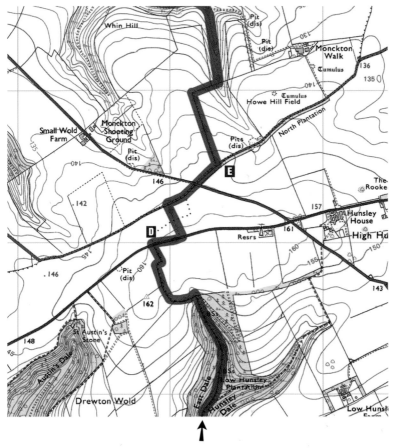

(800 metres), stopping just short of the 2,116-yard (1,935-metre) Drewton Tunnel (now sealed). The path then bears left, away from the railway line and into West Hill Plantation and the lovely East Dale, passing an old stone marker of the Hunsley Fence. The steep climb to the head of the dale marks the end of the path's route across the wooded slopes of the southern Wolds. From here, the Yorkshire Wolds Way crosses wide expanses of chalk tops and follows deep, mainly grassy, dry valleys.

Turn left and follow the field edge round to the B1230 **D**. Cross the busy road with care, turn right along a field-edge path towards the beacon, then left on to another grassy field path. The radio mast that you can see is at High Hunsley and transmits both radio and television to the area. Turn right along Whin Lane, a minor road which is shared with National Cycle Network route 164, then continue ahead over the crossroads into Littlewood Road. Turn left again **E** to follow the field path ahead and then round to the right to descend steeply down through a gate into Swin Dale. This classic dry valley with grazing sheep dominates the walk for the next mile (1.6 km).

The dew pond **3** is of the modern type: concrete-lined rather than built on a man-made saucer of mud or clay as was the practice of Anglo-Danish settlers.

🚏 🚌 *To reach the attractive village of* **North Newbald** *with its two pubs, transport links and interesting church, you need to fork left* **F** *towards the end*

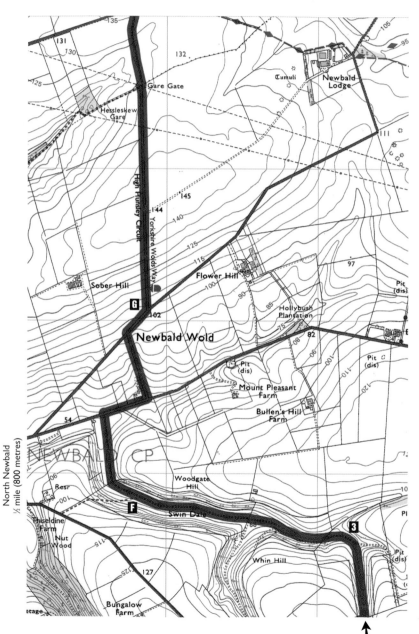

South Cave to Goodmanham/Market Weighton

North Newbald
½ mile (800 metres)

of the dale on a footpath. Where this meets a metalled road, turn right and continue ahead for about ½ mile (800 metres) to the village. To rejoin the trail, leave the village by Beverley Road, the lane that passes the school and Becks Farm, and keep ahead to meet up with the trail as it joins this road from the right at the head of Swin Dale.

Keep ahead through Swin Dale to reach a road at the top of the valley. Turn right on the road, left on a track past a small farm with a smart new building on the corner, right on a minor road, and left again **G** on the Green Lane to Gare Gate, again part of National Cycle Route 164. The path stretches in a straight line now for about 2½ miles (4 km), joining the Sancton–Arras road as it passes Hessleskew Farm **4**. Just before the farm, across the field on the right (no public access), is a group of trees marking the spot of what was a Roman amphitheatre.

Although there are few clearly visible reminders – mainly some barrows and tumuli in fields that are inaccessible to the walker – this part of the Wolds was one of the greatest settlements of the Parisii, late-Iron Age warriors. A square cemetery containing chariots, horse harnesses, skeletons of ponies, bronze brooches, armlets and beads was found a short distance down the Beverley–Market Weighton road.

*To reach the village of **Sancton** and The Star pub/restaurant, turn left at the minor road before the farm and keep ahead for about 2 miles (3.2 km), or take the footpath on the left just before the A1079 which turns into a bridleway track called Dale Road, leading direct to Sancton – a slightly longer route.*

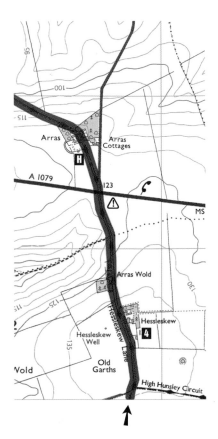

Cross the very busy A1079 with care, taking the farm track directly opposite and then diagonally left **H** to pass between the buildings at Arras, then follow a hedge out into open countryside again. After some distance, keep ahead through the gap in the hedge with the field boundary now on your left. Follow this path through two kissing-gates, eventually descending into a valley known as the Market Weighton Gap to emerge at a minor road junction. Go straight across to keep on the minor road opposite, but beware cyclists on this junction as National Cycle Route 66 crosses our route here. After a short distance you reach another track junction where you have a choice of route.

Main route to Goodmanham

To continue along the Yorkshire Wolds Way towards Goodmanham, walkers should follow the track opposite. Almost immediately you will pass **Rifle Butts Quarry 5** on your right, an important and fascinating geological reserve. Keep on this track, which turns into a metalled lane as it heads northwards into Goodmanham village, turning left on to the main street. The 'finishing post' of this particular section of the National Trail is the small village church **6**.

🚍 🚌 *To visit the rest of the village and the popular Wolds pub the Goodmanham Arms, keep ahead for a short distance just beyond the church.*

Alternative route to Market Weighton

At the junction turn left along the disused railway line **7**. This used to be the Beverley–Market Weighton line and you are joining the Hudson Way, named after the great railway builder George Hudson, and the Wilberforce Way (see 'Other trails', page 31). For most of the route there are high embankments on either side, piled with hawthorn entangled with brambles and nettles. The walker's attention will be diverted by finches, tits and members of the thrush family, in autumn including fieldfare and redwing, which feast off the berries.

As the line reaches the built-up area, another railway joins from the right: it once linked Market Weighton with Driffield. At the end of a development of modern houses **1**, go straight on and you will quickly arrive in the main street of Market Weighton 🚍 🚌 🚌 .

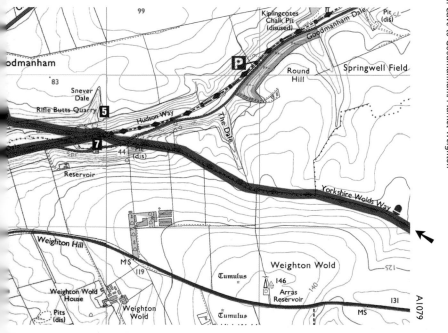

Public transport

North Newbald (1 mile/1.6 km) 🚌
(3 days a week only)
Sancton (2 miles/3.2 km) 🚌
Market Weighton (alt. route) 🚌
Shiptonthorpe (1 mile/1.6 km from alt.
route) 🚌
Taxis/minicabs: South Cave, Market
Weighton

Refreshments and toilets

North Newbald (1 mile/1.6 km) 🍺 The
Gnu, The Tiger
Sancton (2 miles/3.2 km) 🍺 The Star
(closed Mondays)
Goodmanham (on route) 🍺
Goodmanham Arms (limited food)

Market Weighton (alt. route) 🍺 ☕
wide range
Food shops: Market Weighton
Public toilets: Market Weighton

Accommodation

North Newbald (1 mile/1.6 km) 🍺 The Gnu
Sancton (2 miles/3.2 km) Orchard Lodge
(B&B)
Goodmanham (on route) Jubilee House
(B&B), Manor Farm (camping)
Market Weighton (alt. route) Londesborough
Arms Hotel, Red House (B&B), Towthorpe
Grange (near A614, B&B), Weighton Wolds
Cottage
Shiptonthorpe (1 mile/1.6 km from alt.
route) Robeanne House (B&B and camping)

All Saints Church, Goodmanham, built on a site once occupied by a pagan temple.

3 Goodmanham/Market Weighton to Millington

via Londesborough Estate and Nunburnholme

From Goodmanham 8 miles (13 km); from Market Weighton 8.5 miles (13.5 km)

Ascent From Goodmanham: 1,206 ft (368 m); from Market Weighton 1,120 ft (341 m)

Descent From Goodmanham: 1,074 ft (327 m); from Market Weighton 890 ft (271 m)

Highest point Both routes: above Millington 627 ft (191 m)

Lowest point From Goodmanham: Nunburnholme 122 ft (37 m); from Market Weighton: 92 ft (28

Your route is described from two different starting points to correspond with the options at the end of Chapter 2. The two routes come together in the wonderful grounds of the Londesborough Estate. This short section passes through majestic woldland scenery and allows an opportunity to explore the ancient ash woodland of Millington Wood and the unspoilt Millington Pasture. Please note that there are no facilities en route.

Things to look out for

■ **Beverley** A visit to the market town of Beverley and its magnificent Minster, located about 10 miles (16 km) to the east of Market Weighton, is highly recommended. Allow at least half a day to visit the medieval heart of the town and to discover the streets with their fascinating range of names, which give a clear idea of the roles they once played in municipal life: Toll Gavel, Butcher Row, Ladygate, Hengate, Wednesday Market and Saturday Market. The town can be best explored using the excellent Beverley Town Trail, on which you can hunt for 39 carvings and works of art that depict the range of medieval trades.

Beverley Minster ranks as a Gothic masterpiece comparable to the best of cathedrals. Its highlights include a Perpendicular west front, the 14th-century Percy tomb with an elaborately carved canopy, and the nave adorned with carvings of at least 70 musicians. However, if that isn't enough, Beverley boasts another superb church, St Mary's, at the other end of the town. This was founded in the 12th century and drew its prosperity from the Merchants Guilds. It has a chancel ceiling depicting the Kings of England, a 'Minstrels' pillar' and a chapel with a carving of a rabbit with a pilgrim's bag, said to be the inspiration behind Lewis Carroll's White Rabbit.

Opposite St Mary's Church is the historic Beverley Arms Hotel – look out for the Larkin Trail plaque on the front.

For further details on Beverley, contact the Beverley TIC (see page 139).

■ **Skidby Windmill and Museum of East Riding Rural Life** Just 5 miles (8 km) to the south of Beverley lies Skidby Windmill, the only remaining working windmill north of the Humber. For many years the Yorkshire Wolds were the 'breadbasket' of Yorkshire, with over 200 working corn mills in the 19th century. All that remains of this industry now is Grade II listed Skidby, which produces stoneground flour from local wheat. The Museum of East Riding Rural Life in an adjacent warehouse has a display of historic farming implements and machinery from rural East Yorkshire, including a famous 'wolds wagon' built by Sissons and Sons of Leeds.

1 Goodmanham It is difficult to believe that this sleepy village was the scene of a crucial event in the introduction of Christianity to Britain. A heathen temple stood on the site now occupied by the little Norman church when, in AD 626, Edwin, the Saxon King of Northumbria, was converted to the Christian faith by the great missionary Paulinus. Edwin, led by his high priest Coifi, then set about desecrating the temple. The Venerable Bede described 'Goodmundingaham', as it was then called, as 'this one-time place of idols'. Nothing of the temple remains today, but the church, in the centre of this spread-out village, is now most notable for its highly decorative 15th-century font, perhaps the most outstanding in the Wolds. It stands on a short stem and is 5 feet (1.5 metres) high, with rich carving over the bowl's eight sides.

The Goodmanham Arms is a popular, atmospheric pub which gives a warm welcome to walkers. Food is served every lunchtime and Friday evenings.

■ **Kiplingcotes Races** One of the most historic features to be found in the Yorkshire Wolds is the Kiplingcotes Racecourse, home of England's oldest horse race. Although not on the route of the Yorkshire Wolds Way itself, the entire length of the 4-mile (6.4-km) track, covering a rough green lane that has been partly tarmacked on its final section, would make an excellent circular walk from Goodmanham, via Londesborough, Kiplingcotes racecourse and Goodmanham Grange (see the Walking the Riding website for further details).

The date of the first race, as painted on the winning post, was 1519, but the earliest actual record of the race was not until 1555. The Kiplingcotes Derby is still run every year on the third Thursday of March, for prize money that is less

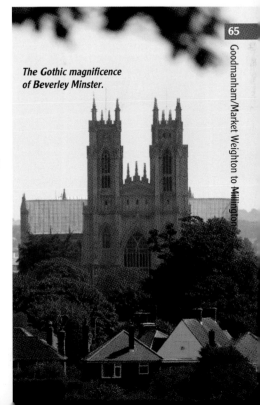

The Gothic magnificence of Beverley Minster.

than £100, being the interest on an endowment provided by 'five noblemen, 19 baronets and 25 gentlemen' in the 17th century.

By horse-racing standards, the Derby is a pretty inelegant affair, with spectators apt to end up with a fair splattering of mud. Most competitors are amateur riders, often from the local farming community. The rules state that horses must be able to 'convey horsemen's weight ten stones, exclusive of saddle, to enter at ye post eleven o'clock on the morning of ye race. The race to be run before two.' The most interesting feature of the Derby is that the person coming second receives more than the winner. He or she gets the entrance money, whereas the victor gets only the interest on the original sum.

In a giant's footstep: William Bradley's amazing boot print on a wall at Market Weighton.

THE
MARKET WEIGHTON
GIANT

THE FOOTPRINT
OF
WILLIAM BRADLEY
THE TALLEST
ENGLISHMAN EVER
RECORDED WHO LIVED
IN THIS HOUSE
BORN 10 FEB 1787
DIED 30 MAY 1820
HEIGHT 7FT 9INS
WEIGHT 27 STONES

ERECTED BY
MARKET WEIGHTON
CIVIC TRUST

2 Market Weighton Once the busiest rail junction in the East Riding outside Hull, with four lines meeting at its now demolished station, as well as being an important crossroads of five main roads, Market Weighton was an extremely busy place until the 1960s. It appeared in Domesday as Wicstun and received a market charter in 1251, but it was mainly a small village which nestled around the 11th-century All Saints Parish Church. Rapid development occurred as a result of the construction of the Market Weighton Canal in 1772. This 11-mile (18-km) waterway to the Humber, which eventually closed in 1900, carried much of the East Riding's agricultural produce and quarried chalk.

John Wesley preached at the Methodist church in Market Place, but perhaps the town's greatest claim to fame was the Yorkshire Giant, William Bradley, who was born here in 1787. He matured to a height of 7 feet 9 inches (2.36 metres), weighed 27 stone (172 kg) and became a celebrated fairground attraction throughout England until his death, due to consumption, at the age of 33. You can see a memorial tablet marking his grave *inside* the parish church – it was feared that grave robbers would steal his remarkable corpse if it was buried in the churchyard. There is also a tablet on the wall of his birthplace (at the top of Linegate) showing the precise size of Bradley's boot. The doorway of the house was specially constructed to take his great bulk.

3 Londesborough Estate The alternative routes from Goodmanham and Market Weighton meet in the great Londesborough Estate. Although now said to be a shadow of its former glory,

The serene waters of the lake are passed on the main route of the trail through the Londesborough Estate.

this is one of the most pleasant spots to be found along the trail. For further information, see page 20.

■ **Cleaving Coombe** A hidden gem of a dry valley tucked just to the east of the trail north of the Londesborough Estate. It is an area of Open Access land and is a haven for wild flowers in late spring. Red kites can be spotted and, if you have time, a short diversion off the trail here is to be recommended.

5 Nunburnholme This is a tiny village with one great claim to fame. The splendid cream-washed rectory, next to St James Church, was the home of the great Victorian ornithologist Francis Orpen Morris. He became rector at Nunburnholme in 1854 when he was in the process of publishing his six-volume *A History of British Birds* and was already busy with a new three-volume work, *A Natural History of the Nests and Eggs of British Birds*. Morris was an

acknowledged pioneer of nature conservation in Victorian times and campaigned for bird protection by writing numerous letters to *The Times*; a collection of these letters was published in 1880. He also wrote authoritative books on British moths as well as an encyclopaedic guide to great country houses in Britain and Ireland. After nearly 40 years at Nunburnholme, Morris died in 1893 at the age of 82. He is buried next to the church door, and in his memory the church bell is inscribed: 'I will imitate your birds by singing'.

Nunburnholme was also home to a Benedictine nunnery, founded by Henry II and dissolved in 1536. Nearby is the largest roost of red kites in East Yorkshire.

■ **Pocklington** A small, bustling market town lying 2 miles (3.2 km) west of the Yorkshire Wolds Way, with a good range of shops and services surrounding All Saints Church.

Pocklington's history can be traced back to the Bronze Age, while in the Iron Age it was the capital of the Parisii tribe. At the time of the Domesday Book, Pocklington was the second largest settlement in Yorkshire after York itself. The Grammar School was founded in 1514 (later, William Wilberforce was its most famous pupil) and the town played an important role in the Tudor rebellion of 1536 that became known as the Pilgrimage of Grace.

On the outskirts of the town lie the Burnby Hall Gardens, home to a national collection of hardy water lilies – the biggest such collection to be found in a natural setting in Europe.

Pocklington Canal is an attractive waterway which runs for 9½ miles (15.3 km) from Canal Head, Pocklington, to the River Derwent. It has a towpath and is a superb location for viewing a wide range of wildlife, from water plants to barn owls.

■ **Warter** The fascinating and picturesque small estate village of Warter lies on the B1246 east of Pocklington (for information about the Warter Estate, see page 21) and a mile (1.6 km) from the trail. It is dominated by the redundant church of St James, which now houses the fascinating Yorkshire Wolds Heritage Centre (see below).

More recently the attractive countryside around Warter has attracted the artist David Hockney. In 2007 he painted his largest work, made up of 50 canvases and measuring 15 by 40 feet (4.6 by 12 metres), entitled *Bigger Trees near Warter*. Other works include *Less Trees near Warter* and *Warter Vista*. You can visit the locations for these paintings

and get a good flavour of the countryside that inspired this great artist on the circular walk described on page 80. Warter is also a good place to start the Pilgrimage of Grace Heritage Trail (see 'Other trails', page 31).

■ **Yorkshire Wolds Heritage Centre** Established in 2006, the Heritage Centre is housed in the attractive but redundant church of St James in Warter. The church, which contains some magnificent Edwardian monuments and four of the finest early 20th-century stained-glass windows, had been threatened with demolition but was saved by the St James Warter Preservation Trust and adapted for use as a cultural, education and heritage centre.

Allow plenty of time to visit the church and churchyard, which often holds special exhibitions and contains useful information and a range of leaflets about local attractions. The Heritage Centre is open daily and serves refreshments on Sunday afternoons throughout summer – see page 140 for contact details.

7 Kilnwick Percy Hall This magnificent country mansion can be spotted to the west of the Yorkshire Wolds Way towards Millington. The area has a long and illustrious history, with evidence of human occupation from the Mesolithic and Neolithic eras. The building has been owned by a succession of powerful landlords and was requisitioned by the military during the Second World War. In 1986 the site was sold to the International Kadampa Buddhist Union. Open to the public as a retreat and for a range of courses in meditation, it usefully provides accommodation and a café.

Burnby Hall Gardens –
the national collection
of water lilies.

Route description

Main route: Goodmanham to Londesborough Park

The path resumes from All Saints Church, **Goodmanham 1**. Turn right down the hill and join the clear dirt track as it goes under the bridge that once carried the Market Weighton–Driffield railway line. Follow the track straight on, curving round the field edge while keeping a drainage ditch on your left. You are surrounded by arable fields as the path swings round to the right, straightens out and after some time emerges at the top of a very large picnic area known as Towthorpe Corner beside the main A614 road, which connects the towns and cities of West Yorkshire with the popular seaside resort of Bridlington. There are timber tables and benches at which to enjoy a break, if you wish, but Yorkshire Wolds Way walkers will soon have a choice of infinitely more peaceful picnic sites as the path traverses **Londesborough Park 3**.

Cross the busy trunk road with care, and join a track – actually part of the Malton to Brough Roman road – through a field, keeping the hedge to your left. The fertile Vale of York spreads out flatly to the west and ahead lie the red roofs of the Londesborough Estate. This track links with a metalled road coming up from the left and proceeds forward into the estate. At the landmark circle of six huge horse chestnut trees, fork left **A** through a kissing-gate and go down the gentle slope, aiming for the left-hand side of the lake through another kissing-gate to ford the stream by a plank bridge. The stream issues into the artificially created Londesborough Lake.

Head up the hill to join a track that merges from the left **B**. This is where the Market Weighton section rejoins the main route.

Alternative route: Market Weighton to Londesborough Park

From the centre of **Market Weighton 2**, the route back to the Yorkshire Wolds Way is found by walking along the York Road from the centre, through a kissing-gate **C** to the right beyond the new housing development, and following a rough path over a field.

Continue ahead through several fields, crossing a series of drainage channels on sleeper bridges on the way. This area is known as Weighton Clay Field. When you reach the busy A614 trunk road, cross with great care and pass through Towthorpe Grange Farm opposite. Beyond the farm, as the track bears left, keep ahead through the kissing-gate into a sheep field. On the left-hand side of the field are a few remains of the deserted medieval village of Towthorpe (see 'Deserted villages', page 19).

Keep ahead through the field with Towthorpe Beck on your right, eventually emerging on to a minor road. Turn left along Intake Hill for a brief distance before turning right through the elegant gates of **Londesborough Park D**.

You will shortly merge with the other part of the Yorkshire Wolds Way at a path junction below the historic deer shelter. This building may have been part of the original Elizabethan mansion, Londesborough Hall, which was demolished in 1819.

A gateway into the Londesborough Estate.

Pass through a gate and walk along the track that curves up the hill to the left, through the trees, to emerge on a street in the attractive estate village of Londesborough. All Saints Church **4**, soon passed on your left, is worth a brief detour. It has a sundial and an 11th-century Anglo-Danish cross above its Norman south door. Beyond the church, turn right uphill and at the crossroads take care and continue straight ahead along the minor road for about a mile (1.6 km). All along this road are excellent views westwards over the Vale of York. These can be enjoyed from the Yorkshire Wolds Way bench, thoughtfully located along the route here. Turn right at the T-junction **D** then left through the farmyard of Partridge Hall. Continue straight ahead through a wooden kissing-gate and over the field, passing Thorns Wood on your left. Go through

the kissing-gate, from which there are fine views over the village of **Nunburnholme 5**, and proceed ahead, keeping a fence on your right. Follow the field edge round **E**, dropping down to a footbridge with kissing-gates at either end over Nunburnholme Beck and through a small field to a road. The Yorkshire Wolds Way turns left, passing the church **6** where the eminent Victorian ornithologist Francis Orpen Morris was rector from 1854 until 1893. It is worth entering the church to see the fine Anglo-Saxon cross.

Beyond the church, turn right off the road and follow the field edges on to another road. Turn left on the road to continue up the slope, and very soon fork right **F** on the track through Bratt Wood. At the top of the hill go through a gate and cross a field, keeping the fence to your right.

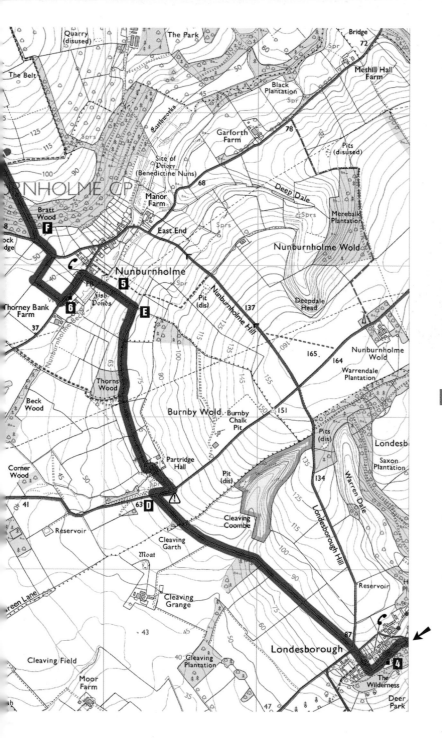

Then go through a gate to another field and a track serving Wold Farm. At the farm **G** bear left down a limestone track to join a metalled lane and continue ahead for about 100 yards (91 metres). Turn sharp right by the house, go up the field and turn left to meet the B1246 road which links **Pocklington** with **Warter**. Cross the road through a bridle gate and follow the path leading to the top of the plantation ahead.

Go through a bridle gate and continue through open fields with the mansion of **Kilnwick Percy** **7** visible on your left. You may be lucky to spot red kites overhead in this area. Pass through Low Warrendale Farm on a track to join a road at a right-angle bend **H**.

🦆 *Turn left and head for about ½ mile (800 metres) along the road to reach the tiny hamlet of Kilnwick Percy. Turn left and a further ¼ mile (400 metres) will bring you to Kilnwick Percy Hall, which is a Buddhist Retreat Centre and World Peace Café (open most days, but check details).*

The Yorkshire Wolds Way now turns right up the hillside to begin one of the most memorable sections on the whole of the route. Behind are fine long-distance views to the west. The flat Vale of York floor has three sets of power-station cooling towers: Drax to the left, Eggborough in the middle and Ferrybridge to the right.

At the end of the plantation, turn sharp left to cross the field, then left again **I** to reach the edge of the hillside overlooking Millington **8**. On a clear day the views are extensive. The line of the Pennine Hills is clearly visible and the towers of York Minster can be seen, as can the edge of the North York Moors near Sutton Bank. Look very carefully and you may even see the White Horse of Kilburn, a huge turf-cut figure on the hillside above the village of Kilburn.

Below is a bird's-eye view of Millington nestling at the foot of the chalk escarpment. The small fields divided by ancient hedges are very striking and indicate what so much of the Wolds landscape must have looked like after the Enclosure Acts of the 18th/19th century had been implemented. Turn right along the edge of the hill, which

74

Goodmanham/Market Weighton to Millington

Public transport
Londesborough (on route) 🚌 (infrequent)
Pocklington (2 miles/3.2 km) 🚌
Taxis/minicabs: Pocklington

Refreshments and toilets
Pocklington (2 miles/3.2 km) 🍴
🦆 good range
Kilnwick Percy (1 mile/1.6 km)
🦆 World Peace Café
Millington (¾ mile/1.2 km) 🍴 Gait Inn,
🦆 Ramblers Rest (closed Tues/Wed)
Food shops: Pocklington
Public toilets: Pocklington

Accommodation
Pocklington (2 miles/3.2 km)
Feathers Hotel, Ashfield Farm (B&B 3 miles/4.8 km), Yorkway Motel (on A1079), South Lea Caravan Park (camping)
Kilnwick Percy (1 mile/1.6 km)
Paws a While (B&B), Wolds Retreat (B&B), Low Warrendale Farm (camping)
Millington (¾ mile/1.2 km)
Laburnum Cottage (B&B), Ramblers Rest (B&B), Millington Village Hall (bunkbarn)

constitutes a magnificent promenade overlooking one of the least spoilt of the Wolds' dales.

To reach your destination, leave the Yorkshire Wolds Way just before you reach Warren Farm. Look out for a footpath on the left heading downhill towards Millington – part of the Minster Way (see 'Other trails', page 31). Go through the kissing-gate and head downwards, crossing two fields and a wooden boardwalk over Millington Beck, through a small farm to emerge in the small village of Millington.

🚪🍵 *Turn left to reach the centre of Millington.*

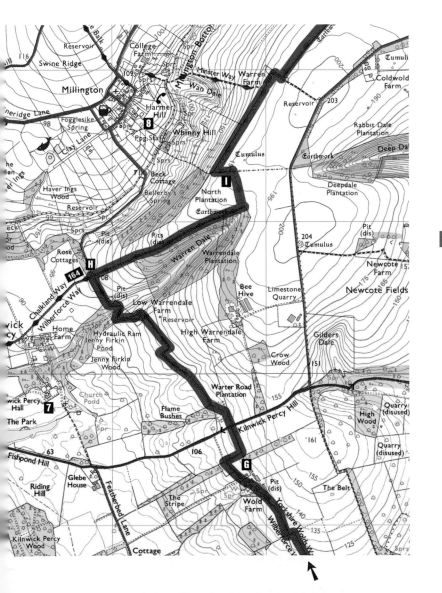

The stunning Kilnwick Percy Hall, now a
Buddhist meditation centre, can be seen
from the trail near Millington.

David Hockney and the Yorkshire Wolds

There is one person who has recently raised the profile of this superb and vastly underrated part of East Yorkshire. The influential artist David Hockney, the Yorkshire-born painter, designer and photographer, has been producing stunning works of art in the Yorkshire Wolds countryside.

David Hockney was born in Bradford in 1937 and became interested in books and art from an early age. He went to Bradford College of Art between 1953 and 1957, then studied at the Royal College of Art alongside artists Peter Blake and Allen Jones, developing his skills in 'abstract expressionism'.

In the 1960s he was drawn to California, where he produced a series of paintings of swimming pools in the form of large icon prints, as in *The Bigger Splash*. He also experimented with photo-montages of the interior of homes to produce collages that he called 'joiners'.

During the 1970s he worked with photography and in costume design for theatre whilst painting fewer pictures. He began to paint more in the 1980s, but also developed a keen interest in introducing technology into his artwork by using photocopiers, fax machines and laser printers. Hockney has continued to

experiment widely with the latest computer technology and has recently produced many works of art using the 'brushes app' on iPads and iPhones. In 2011 he held an exhibition in Canada which consisted exclusively of 100 flower images using this latest computer medium.

Hockney and the Wolds

It was during the 1990s, when he returned to England regularly to visit his elderly mother and terminally ill friend Jonathan Silver, that Hockney started to paint in the countryside of the Yorkshire Wolds. He was spending so much time in Yorkshire that in 2005 he set up his studio in Bridlington and made the town a base for producing works of art.

He painted at locations along the line of the Yorkshire Wolds from Warter northwards, close to the trail near Millington, Huggate, Fridaythorpe and Thixendale. He was also fascinated by the landscape inland from Bridlington towards the village of Kilham, along the line of an old Roman road known as Woldgate. He delighted in painting avenues or tunnels of trees and views through the seasons (see Kilham and Woldgate, page 121).

Hockney created his monumental and visually stunning piece *Bigger Trees near Warter* in 2007. This enormous work of art, measuring 40 feet (12 metres) by 15 feet (4.5 metres), was created out of 50 individual canvases and illustrates a copse of trees in the countryside near the village of Warter. (The location is a short distance off the Yorkshire Wolds Way, near Nunburnholme, but can be visited on the circular walk on page 80.) Another nearby copse that Hockney painted was famously felled before he could complete the picture.

Bigger Trees near Warter and other works have been put on show at the Royal Academy, but it was a major exhibition at the same venue in early 2012, entitled *A Bigger Picture* and showing 150 of Hockney's works, that attracted huge numbers and raised the profile of this previously unsung landscape.

The Hockney Trail in Yorkshire is a driving route established to help visitors discover the locations of the artist's major works along the back lanes of the Yorkshire Wolds countryside – see page 139.

The tunnel of trees along the Roman road known as Woldgate, which was painted by David Hockney through the seasons.

A Circular Walk in Hockney Country

A circular walk of approximately 8 miles (12.8 km) starting at the Yorkshire Wolds Heritage Centre in the redundant but majestic church of St James in the attractive estate village of **Warter** (see pages 21 and 68). The walk offers superb views over open countryside and secluded valleys and passes the location for one of David Hockney's most famous paintings, **_Bigger Trees near Warter_**. There is a choice of route towards the end of the walk, to take in either a couple of Hockney locations, including a fabulous view over Warter, or to experience the wonderfully secluded dry valley of Great Dug Dale. Although there is quite a lot of road-walking on both routes, especially towards the end, most of it is on quiet rural roads with little traffic. Allow time to explore the picturesque village with its attractive estate cottages and to visit the **Heritage Centre** located in **St James Church**.

There are no pubs, cafés or shops either in Warter village or en route, but the Wolds Heritage Centre, which is open daily, has toilet facilities. When planning your walk, note that the Heritage Centre does serve tea and cakes on Sunday afternoons between mid-July and mid-September only. (For contact details, see page 140.) There is a large car park in the village next to the Warter Church of England Primary School. Warter is located 4½ miles (7 km) along the B1246 between Pocklington and Bainton. The 743/744 bus between York and Bridlington passes through the village.

From the Heritage Centre walk carefully eastwards along the B1246, passing a pond on your left, before taking the first minor road on your left signed to Huggate and Wetwang. This quiet road climbs steadily up **Scarndale Hill**, with views opening up. You may be able to spot the location of old village houses in the uneven ground in the field on your left.

Where the road turns to the left, keep ahead in the same direction on a bridleway into fields, with the hedge boundary on your right-hand side. After a short while turn left, with the hedge boundary now on your left.

At a bridleway junction, turn right towards a small plantation. Here magnificent views begin to open up in all directions. To the west you can see the cooling towers of Ferrybridge and Drax in industrial West Yorkshire, while to the south-east the land drops away towards the **Humber Estuary**. The lofty position commands a huge expanse of sky – great for viewing cloud formations and sunsets.

The path continues north-eastwards along the bridleway, with plantations on the left and open fields on the right, before steeply descending through a gate into the beautiful and peaceful **Lavender Dale**. Both this valley and the adjoining **Brig Dale** can be fully explored as they are on Open Access land. At the bottom, turn left along the tarmac path and follow the valley floor of Lavender Dale. In late spring and summer look for wild flowers, especially orchids, cowslips and field scabious. At a valley junction, with the V-shaped Brig Dale ahead, take the right-hand fork.

At the end of Brig Dale, turn right through a gate along a bridleway and follow the wide hedge-lined track towards a stand of trees. Turn left through another gate, still on the bridleway, and head towards the buildings of Blanch Farm. Owned by the **Warter Estate**, this farm was once used as a grange by the Cistercian Abbey of Meaux near Beverley.

Keasey Dale
Earthworks
Saintofts Dale
Saintofts Plantation
Keasey Farm
Houseclose Plantation
Scatter Dale
Brig Dale
Blanch Farm
Tumulus
Keasey Plantation
Dearsden
Minningdale Farm
Hollows
Ringlands Plantation
Minningdale Plantation
Lavender Dale
Meadows Dale
The Meadows
Racedale Plantation
Minningdale
Warter Wold
Minning Dale
Ringlands
Three Corner Plantation
Blanch Wood
Thirty Acres
Thirty Acre Plantation
Race Dale
Golden Valley
Scarn Dale
Blanch Dale Plantation
WARTER CP
The Wolds
Scarndale Hill
Site of Priory (Augustinian)
Rickman Hill Farm
Earthworks
Townend Wood
Dalton Gates Farm
Pit (dis)
Dalton Gates
Bucksey Bridge
Middlebridge Farm
Hungerhill Closes
The Brambles
Middleton Road Plantation
Shiptondale Farm
Dalton Gates Cottage
Ludhill Spring
Lady Spring
Bailey Dale
Great Dug Dale
Milldale Plantation
Hunger Hill
Moss Hill Wood
Dugdale Fields
Farberry Garth Farm
Loaningdale
Reservoir
Quarry (dis)
Loaningdale Farm
A
B
1246

Warter Vista, *2006*.

Go through another gate to pass a farm building, then turn right on a surfaced footpath which is part of the Minster Way, linking York and Beverley (see page 31). You are now passing through arable fields with good views towards the Humber Estuary, where you may spot the **Humber Bridge** and, to your left, the lighthouse at **Flamborough Head** on a clear day.

This 'Warter Vista' was taken in early September, with the church spire visible ahead of distant, now harvested, fields and the maize crop more developed than in the painting.

Where the Minster Way heads off to your left, keep ahead on this track, going southwards towards the B1246. When you reach the road, go straight across with care and keep the boundary on your left as you continue along the footpath through fields towards a plantation of trees. These trees are known as the **Middleton Road Plantation** and have been 'immortalised' by David Hockney in his enormous and famous canvas *Bigger Trees near Warter*, which he produced to critical acclaim in 2007. Go through a gate and turn right on to the minor road just before the plantation and follow this road to the T-junction, where you turn left on another minor road signed Burnby and Market Weighton. Immediately after the junction, look to your left at the view of **Dalton Cottage** and the trees – this was the place where Hockney painted

82

his enormous canvas. Continue on this road towards another stand of trees and follow it round the right-hand bend.

Here you have a choice of routes:

Option **A**, the main route, follows minor roads back to Warter, taking in another classic Hockney view.

Option **B** is an alternative and slightly shorter route with less overall road-walking and taking in the lovely and peaceful Great Dug Dale. However, there is a longer walk at the end along the busy B1246 back into Warter.

For the main route, **A**, keep on this minor road, ignoring the turn on the left towards Market Weighton. Just before you reach Loaningdale Farm turn right on the road signed Warter 1½ miles, Huggate 4½ miles. In 2009 Hockney commenced his *Less Trees near Warter* at the roadside by this junction, but sadly the plantation of beech trees he was painting was felled before he could complete the work – he had to finish it using computer graphics.

Keep on this road as you descend Hunger Valley towards Warter, taking in the magnificent views of the village and distinctive spire of **St James Church**, surrounded by the classic countryside of the Yorkshire Wolds. As you pass the Open Access land of **Bailey Dale** on your right you are close to the location where Hockney painted *Warter Vista* in 2006. Keep on this road to enter the village of Warter opposite the pond and turn left to return to the start along the busy B1246.

For the alternative route, **B**, keep ahead on the minor road and, after about 50 yards (45 metres), turn right on the footpath through a gate and around the field edge to the left. The superb dry valley of **Great Dug Dale** now opens up to your left.

Keep ahead to remain above the valley, with the fence line on your left, and descend slowly in a gentle curving arc. Look out for the large rock on your left, which has been the subject of many local stories. It may have been placed by a past owner of the Warter Estate as a convenient seat, it could be glacial in origin, or possibly it marks the spot where a Second World War bomber crashed. You then drop more steeply through some beech woodland and finally through a kissing-gate to meet the B1246. Turn left and walk back towards Warter village, taking care on the blind bends.

Bigger Trees near Warter, *2007.*

4 Millington to Thixendale

via Fridaythorpe
12 miles (19 km)

Ascent 1,869 feet (570 metres)
Descent 1,776 feet (541 metres)
Highest point Gill's Farm 691 feet (211 metres)
Lowest point Millington 255 feet (78 metres)

This is a superb section of the trail in the heart of Wolds country. There are many wonderful dry valleys to enjoy and the villages of Huggate, just off the route, and Fridaythorpe, marking the halfway point of the trail, give added interest. The dramatic beauty of Thixendale and the approach to Thixendale village memorably complete the stage. Apart from village pubs, there are few facilities en route.

Things to look out for

1 Millington The starting point for this section, Millington is delightfully located in a valley just off the Yorkshire Wolds Way. It is an enchanting village surrounded by magnificent countryside. There is evidence of settlement in the area dating back to Roman times and the 12th-century church of St Margaret has a modern window depicting walkers on the road to Emmaus. The village has a welcoming pub called the Gait Inn – named after the traditional method of dividing up land on Millington Pasture (see below) and the popular Ramblers Rest Tearoom (closed on Tuesdays and Wednesdays).

In 2004 David Hockney painted *A Wider Valley Millington* just outside the village.

2 Millington Pasture and Millington Wood The steep-sided valley of Millington Dale has been a popular local beauty spot for decades and the classic chalk banks and tops of Millington Pasture were, until the 1960s, uncultivated downland. Totalling over 400 acres (162 hectares) of close-cropped grass meadow, the Pasture was the last surviving example of the traditional way of open-pasture sheep-grazing in the Wolds. It was divided among 108 local farmers, each one awarded a 'gait' or 'gate' comprising pasture for six sheep, or four sheep plus two lambs. Despite a public outcry and mass rambles by local walkers, fences were erected along the narrow road running through the Dale bottom. This ended the hitherto unrestricted access, and some crops were sown on the higher ground. Nevertheless, the Pasture is still one of the few parts of the Wolds to convey a sense of being in a natural landscape, and it can be enjoyed by walkers taking a circular route from Millington village.

Millington Wood, one of the few remaining wooded dales in the Wolds, lies nearby. It is primarily classic ancient ash woodland and, as such, is a Site of Special Scientific Interest. A path starts from a picnic site and car park and runs right through the woods, enabling you to enjoy a nature walk.

■ **Bishop Wilton** This attractive small village on the western flank of the Yorkshire Wolds is passed through by two walking routes: the Minster Way and Chalkland Way (see 'Other trails', page 31). Just to the north lies Garrowby Hill, the highest point on the Yorkshire Wolds at 807 feet (246 metres). David Hockney painted the view from the top in his picture *Garrowby Hill* in 1998.

The village is popular with walkers, with a wonderful range of walks, and an excellent pub, The Fleece, serves food and has accommodation. The medieval church of St Edith was much restored in the 19th century and is a Sykes Church, but not on the Sykes Churches Trail (see page 94).

Winter sunshine near Millington.

Ramsons, more commonly known as wild garlic, grow profusely in Millington Woods in late spring and can be easily identified by their pungent aroma.

3 Huggate Located just off the route, and despite being in a hollow, Huggate is the highest village in the Wolds at 558 feet (170 metres). It has a welcoming pub, the Wolds Inn, which naturally claims to be the highest pub in the Yorkshire Wolds. At the centre of the village are a large green and a pond on one of the few natural clay basins to have formed above the chalk. St Mary's Church has the locally rare feature of a spire on its 14th-century tower, which dominates the surrounding countryside. The village is notorious for being cut off for several days at a time after winter snowstorms, since all approach roads involve steep inclines and exposed stretches that suffer from extensive drifting.

In 2005 David Hockney painted the view towards the village in *Huggate's St Mary's Church Spire*.

5 Fridaythorpe This is one of the largest villages in the Wolds and, as the suffix 'thorpe' suggests, was established by Danish invaders. It is possible that the first half of the name was derived from the Norse goddess of love, Freya. Today's Fridaythorpe is a miscellany of houses dating from the past three centuries. St Mary's Church, behind a farm, is worth seeking out for its south doorway (*c.*1120), which Pevsner described as 'utterly barbaric'. It has a jumble of columns, chip-carving, a rope motif, rosettes and decorated scallops. St Mary's Church is on the Sykes Churches Trail (see page 94).

Located on the busy A166 trunk road between York and Driffield, Fridaythorpe has good public transport connections, a café and a pub, the Farmers Arms. It is the approximate halfway point along the Yorkshire Wolds Way.

■ **Fimber** This peaceful village lies 2 miles (3.2 km) north-east of Fridaythorpe. The Victorian church of St Mary was built in a 13th-century style on the site of a Bronze Age burial mound. It is one of the churches on the Sykes Churches Trail (see page 94). The Yorkshire Wolds Railway has ambitious plans to open a short stretch of the disused Malton to Driffield line from the old Fimber station towards Wetwang.

■ **Driffield** A busy market town, Driffield, also called Great Driffield, is located about 9 miles (14.4 km) east of

the trail from Fridaythorpe. It is known as the Capital of the Yorkshire Wolds and holds one of the best agricultural shows in the country. The tower of the 500-year-old church of All Saints dominates the area, but it was the arrival of the canal and railway that allowed the town to expand. There is a good range of pubs and places to stay and some attractive town walks – especially around the canal.

■ **Kirby Underdale** Located on the western edge of the Wolds, about 3 miles (4.8 km) west of Thixendale, this small village has a church, All Saints, which dates from the 12th century and sits in a wonderfully remote location. Look out for a small Roman carving which may represent Mercury.

Route description

Retrace your steps from **Millington 1** eastwards along the Minster Way up the hillside to rejoin the Yorkshire Wolds Way through the kissing-gate near Warren Farm. Turn left and the trail soon passes to the right of Warren Farm and after a short dog-leg continues ahead with the hedge on the right. Opposite is **Millington Wood**, and north of that can be seen the slopes of **Millington Pasture 2**. Where the path overlooks Sylvan Dale **A**, swing down to the left, through a kissing-gate and then steeply down to the valley floor. The name 'Sylvan Dale' suggests a time

when this and other Wolds valleys were more heavily tree-covered. Today, the scrub-covered slopes remain largely untouched by plough or fertiliser and often accommodate a wide range of wild flowers with their attendant butterflies and birds.

From the valley floor, a delightful, peaceful spot, the path strikes steeply straight up the opposite side on steps – the steepest climb so far – to a gate and then continues ahead along the field edge. On the left can be seen the line of a substantial earthwork **3** which was constructed by the La Tène tribesmen in the late Iron Age.

Millington to Thixendale

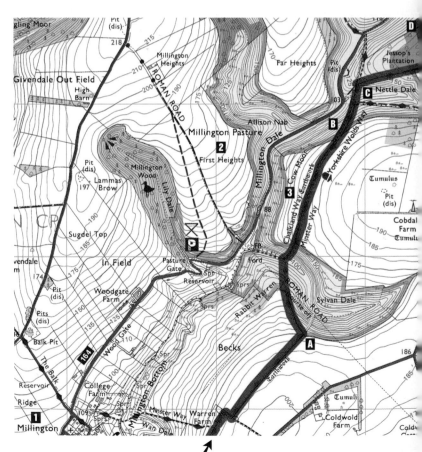

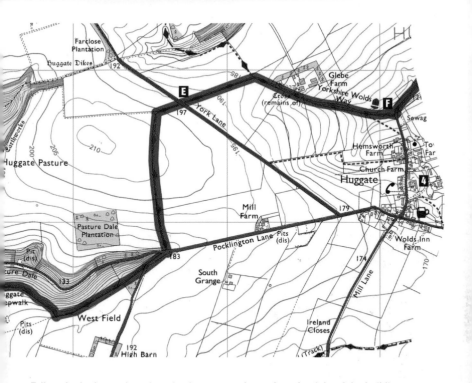

Follow the hedge and earthwork where they descend left **B** down into Nettle Dale before climbing again up the opposite slope for a short distance, then bearing right **C** on a more gradual slope towards Jessop's Plantation. This is a wonderful path with superb views. Walk around the edge of the plantation and turn right **D** across Huggate Sheepwalk, which winds majestically above Pasture Dale, to a road. Turn left and walk along this to the junction, where you follow the signs across the road. From here, when visibility is perfect, it is possible to see as far away as Lincoln Cathedral, the towers of the Humber Bridge and Sheffield in the south, York Minster to the west, and the lighthouse on Flamborough Head to the east.

Cross York Lane **E** and follow the farm road, passing Glebe Farm. Look out for the path to the right of the buildings themselves before returning to the track. On the hillside ahead you can see a diamond-shaped plantation. Larch was planted here to celebrate Queen Victoria's Diamond Jubilee in 1897, but the plantation was felled for mine props during the Second World War and an assortment of trees and bushes grew in their place, preserving, to some extent, the original diamond motif on the hillside. Huggate Church spire is now visible on your right.

When you reach the road junction **F**, the Yorkshire Wolds Way turns left towards Fridaythorpe.

To visit the pub and the village of **Huggate 4**, *turn right and the village centre is ½ mile (800 metres) along the road.*

After turning left, head up the tarmac road then turn left on to the field edge before Northfield House. At the end of the field go through the gate and descend gradually into Horse Dale and, at the bottom, curve to the left up the chalk valley of Holm Dale. You are now amongst truly magnificent woldland scenery, which can be fully appreciated from the new benches complete with appropriately uplifting poetry. Near the junction of the two dales **5** is the site of one of the many medieval villages wiped out by the Black Death (see 'Deserted villages', page 19).

The path reaches the dale head and you proceed through a gate near two distinctive horse chestnut trees on a track that emerges on the main street **G** of **Fridaythorpe** **G** 🚌. Turn right and then left on the road by 🍺 the Farmers Arms, signposted to Thixendale.

Passing the attractive new bus shelter, another local project which is part of the 'Wander – Art on the Yorkshire Wolds Way' scheme, and the pond, look out for the wooden sign commemorating the 21st anniversary of the Yorkshire Wolds Way on Thursday, 2 October 2003. It records that Hessle Haven is 39 miles (63 km) away to the south and that Filey Cliffs are 40 miles (64 km) to the north, making Fridaythorpe the approximate halfway mark. Continue ahead along Thixendale Road and turn left on a track 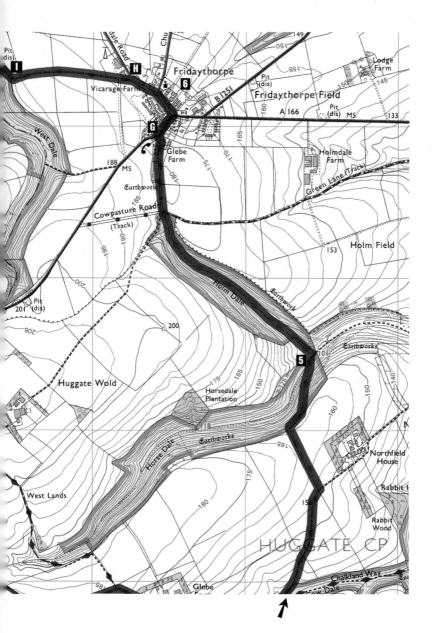 just before the large modern mill and cross the access road. After following the edge of several fields the path turns right to descend, at an angle, into West Dale with wonderful views. Bear right at the bottom 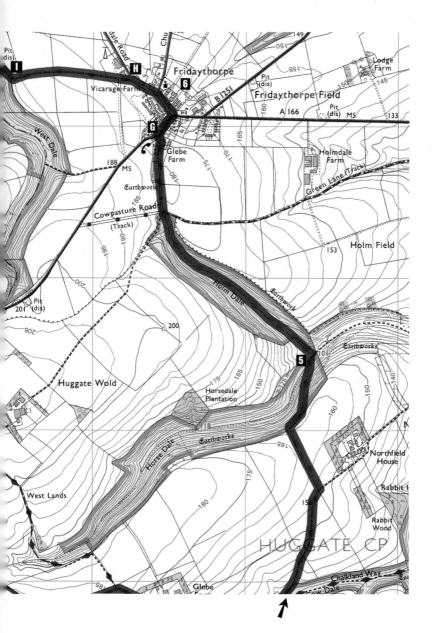,

The swirling sculpture Time and Flow *by artist Chris Drury can be found at the junction of Thixen Dale and Worm Dale.*

then left up a small tributary valley, through a kissing-gate on to a track. Where the track bears left, keep ahead on the field edge to join the road on the north side of Gill's Farm. Cross the road and after a short distance the route bends down through a field gate into magnificent Thixen Dale **J**, regarded by some as one of the most enjoyable parts of the Yorkshire Wolds Way. Dramatically located at the junction of Thixen Dale and Worm Dale ahead is a new artwork by the artist Chris Drury, a swirling pattern in the landscape called *Time and Flow*.

Almost turn back on yourself at the bottom of the valley and follow the line of trees through two gates down the chalk valley **7**. After passing through one further gate, walk along a rutted track to the road. Steep, uncultivated banks of grasses and wild flowers rise on either side. Skylarks and yellowhammers are everywhere in spring and summer, as are peacefully grazing lambs and sheep.

To visit the gallery of renowned wildlife artist Robert Fuller, turn left at the junction and walk about ⅓ mile (500 metres) to Fotherdale Farm.

Turn right and follow the tarmac lane for about ½ mile (800 metres) before turning left into the main street of Thixendale **8**. The Cross Keys Inn is immediately on the right, just off the main road.

Public transport

Fridaythorpe (on route)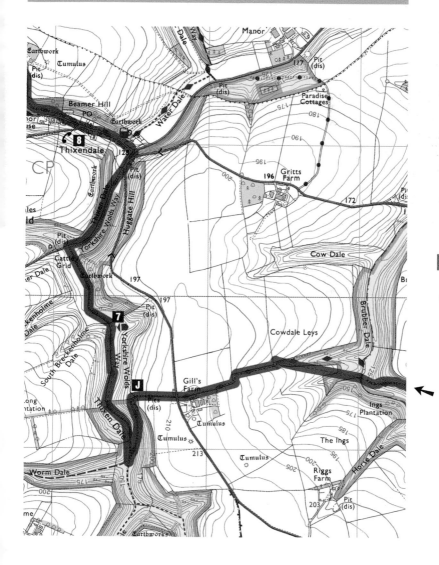

Refreshments and toilets

Bishop Wilton (3¾ miles/6 km) 🚻
Fleece Inn
Huggate (¼ mile/400 metres) 🚻 Wolds Inn
Fridaythorpe (on route) 🚻 Farmers
Arms ☕ Seaways Café
Thixendale (on route) 🚻 Cross Keys

Accommodation

Bishop Wilton (3¾ miles/6 km) Beckside
Cottage (B&B), Fleece Inn (B&B)
Huggate (¼ mile/400 metres) Greenwick Farm
(B&B), Manor House Farm (B&B), Wolds Inn
(B&B, camping), Home on the Wolds (B&B)
Fimber (2¼ miles/3.6 km) Fimber Gate (B&B)
Sledmere (6 miles/9.6 km) Life Hill Farm (B&B)
Thixendale (on route) Manor Farm (B&B),
Cross Keys (B&B)

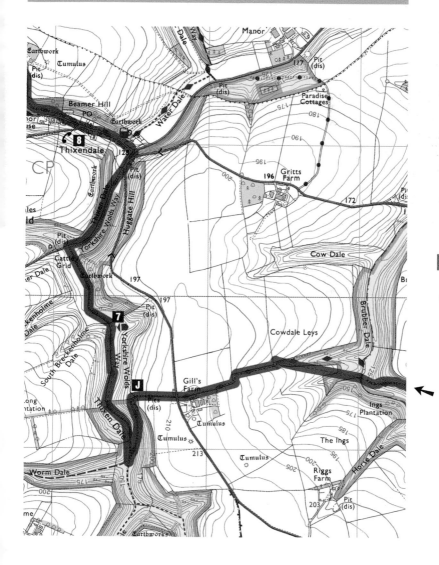

93

Millington to Thixendale

The Sykes Churches Trail

The Sykes Churches Trail is a driving route that has been devised by the East Yorkshire Historic Churches Group, visiting a selection of the superb 'Sykes' churches in villages of the Yorkshire Wolds. These churches are so named as they were all restored or rebuilt by the Sykes family of the Sledmere Estate between the mid-19th century and the First World War. The map shows the northern and southern routes of the trail, which is mainly on minor roads through the magnificent rolling country of the Yorkshire Wolds.

All the churches are worth visiting, but the following are especially interesting:

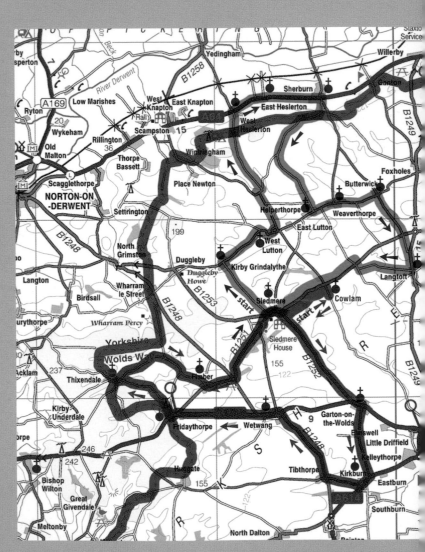

Southern route

St Mary, Sledmere
(also start of northern route)

Standing immediately behind Sledmere House, St Mary's is a grand church befitting the importance of the Sykes family. Completely rebuilt in 1893–8 in a lavish Gothic style and at huge cost, it has many Sykes memorials, an elaborate reredos and a vaulted south porch.

St Michael and all Angels, Garton on the Wolds

This is essentially two churches in one. The first, forming the exterior, is Norman with a bold west tower. Inside is the astonishing second church, restored in 1872 and decorated with highly colourful murals and wonderful stained glass in an impressive early Gothic style. The famous architectural historian Nikolaus Pevsner was a great admirer of the interior of this church.

St Mary, Kirkburn

Another Pevsner favourite, St Mary's is a superb Norman church with a magnificent carved font. It was restored in 1856–7 with the addition of a south porch; further work including a marble reredos and wooden screen followed.

Northern route

St Andrew, Kirby Grindalythe

This 12th-century church with its prominent spire was restored by Sir Tatton Sykes in 1872–5, at which time the west wall of the nave was covered in a gilded Italian mosaic depicting the Ascension.

St Peter, Langtoft

Look out for the drum-shaped Norman carved font, which was moved here from the church at the nearby abandoned village of Cottam (see 'Deserted villages', page 19).

You can find more information on the full Sykes Churches Trail and download leaflets for the northern and southern routes from the East Yorkshire Historic Churches Group website: www.eychurches.org.uk

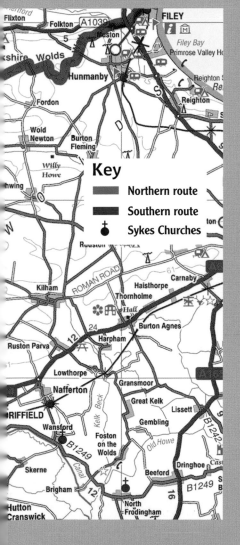

Key

Northern route

Southern route

♱ Sykes Churches

Ornate carvings decorate the entrance to
St Mary's Church, Sledmere, the
grandest of all the Sykes Churches.

The simple church of St Mary, Thixendale, was built in the 1860s.

Sykes Churches Trail

The highly decorated interior of St Michael and All Angels Church, Garton on the Wolds.

5 Thixendale to Sherburn

via Wharram Percy, Wharram le Street and Wintringham

19 miles (30 km)

Ascent 2,180 feet (664 metres)

Descent 2,474 feet (754 metres)

Highest point Vessey Pasture 708 feet (216 metres)

Lowest point Wintringham 137 feet (42 metres)

This long section passes through some of the least-frequented countryside in the Wolds – the long northern scarp that rises above Wintringham – but also passes one of the most popular tourist 'honeypots' in the Yorkshire Wolds: the deserted medieval village of Wharram Percy. When planning your walk try to allow plenty of time to explore and enjoy the wonderfully peaceful setting of the lost village. However, please allow for the fact that there are very few facilities on this section, and the shop at Thixendale stocks only a very limited range. You may wish to consider stopping either at North Grimston, near Wharram le Street, or at Wintringham and breaking this section up into two shorter stages. As Wintringham has no facilities, you can either take a taxi to the market town of Malton or walk to the nearby village of Rillington on the A64, which has two pubs and where you can pick up a regular bus or taxi to Malton. There is also limited accommodation in Thorpe Bassett near Rillington. Before Sherburn there is a very short alternative route to take walkers to the popular Yorkshire Wolds Way Caravan and Campsite.

Things to look out for

1 Thixendale There is no more tranquil village in the Yorkshire Wolds than Thixendale. Its mix of traditional and modern dwellings sits peacefully on either side of a single lane that hugs the floor of a straight chalk valley. Contours climb steeply all around, and the serene harmony of birdsong and sheep echoes over the pantile roofs throughout spring and summer. The only way into the village is by narrow lanes or along footpaths through green dales that have stayed unchanged for centuries.

Six major dales clearly converge here, but, with a bit of time spent studying a large-scale map, it is possible to trace a total of sixteen dales, like the spokes of a wheel, radiating out from the village. This may be the origin of the name 'Thixendale'.

The village has an excellent pub, the Cross Keys, and a small shop in the former post office which sells a limited range of snacks. Thixendale was once served by the church at Wharram Percy, but when that was abandoned there was no longer a place of worship. St Mary's

Church was not built until 1870 and was the work of the Wolds church architect and restorer G. E. Street, paid for by the second Sir Tatton Sykes of Sledmere (see Sykes Churches, page 22). He also provided the excellent lychgate, vicarage and school, the latter now used as a village hall.

David Hockney visited the Thixendale area in 2005 and 2007 and painted *Wheatfield near Fridaythorpe* and *Three Trees near Thixendale*.

2 Wharram Percy The original route of the Yorkshire Wolds Way bypassed what is indisputably one of the most interesting historical features to be seen along the footpath. Fortunately, the present route passes right through the middle of this fascinating site. Wharram Percy is the best-preserved ruin of a deserted medieval village in England – for details, see 'Deserted medieval villages', page 19.

5 Wharram le Street A tiny hamlet on the Yorkshire Wolds Way near Wharram Percy, Wharram le Street is located on the line of the old Roman road between Malton and Beverley, hence the suffix 'le Street'. The church of St Mary's was much restored in Victorian times but originally dates from the 12th century.

6 Duggleby Howe At this huge round barrow, 20 feet (6 metres) high and 120 feet (37 metres) in diameter, the remains of 50 late-Neolithic cremations have been found, plus an assortment of flint arrowheads, tools carved from boars' and beavers' teeth, and bone pins. It lies 200 yards (185 metres) south of Duggleby Church, just off the B1253.

Thixendale, favourite of all villages for many Yorkshire Wolds Way walkers, nestles snugly in its valley.

99

Thixendale to Sherburn

■ **Howardian Hills** This Area of Outstanding Natural Beauty (AONB) lies to the west of the Yorkshire Wolds, between the North York Moors and the Vale of York, and the hills have been recognised nationally for their rolling character, pastoral landscapes and historic country estates. Highlights include the magnificent Castle Howard and Nunnington Hall, and there are many walks available to help explore this area. For details, visit the excellent Howardian Hills AONB website (see page 139).

■ **North Grimston** This small village lies to the west of the trail near Wharram le Street. The 12th-century church of St Nicholas has a highly decorative and superbly carved font. The village used to be served by the Malton to Driffield railway line up until the 1950s. The Middleton Arms pub is open daily except Christmas and also provides accommodation.

■ **Sledmere** Roughly 6 miles (9.6 km) east of the Wharram part of the trail, this small estate village is dominated by Sledmere House, an elegant Georgian country house, the ancestral home to the Sykes family (see 'Large country estates', page 22). The village can boast a fine pub, the Triton Arms, while the 14th-century church of St Mary has some wonderful carvings and an Eleanor Cross. Sledmere Church is the largest and grandest Sykes church and start point of the Sykes Churches Trail (see page 94). The well-kept estate-workers' cottages add a timeless feel to the village.

7 Wintringham St Peter's Church, Wintringham, is constructed from the same seam of Tadcaster limestone that was used to build York Minster and its most fascinating feature is the stained-glass windows of the aisle, each one depicting a 14th-century saint on a white background stained yellow. Such rich glaziery is considered rare outside

Looking down on the village and church of East Heslerton from the northern scarp of the Yorkshire Wolds.

100

Thixendale to Sherburn

York. The carving of the pews, pulpit and screens is Jacobean. The well-preserved church dates mainly from the 14th and 15th centuries and has survived partly due to the help of the Churches Conservation Trust.

Seek out the following instruction to bellringers provided by Michael Gill, the clerk, in 1723:

I pray you Gentlemen beware
And when you ring ye Bells take care;
For he that Rings and breaks a stay,
Must pay Sixpence without delay.
And if you ring in Spurs or Hatt
You must likewise pay Sixpence for that.

■ **Rillington** A large village split by the busy A64 about 2 miles (3.2 km) from Wintringham. It has two pubs – the Fleece and the Coach and Horses. The parish church of St Andrew has Norman origins. Nearby is the wonderful Regency country mansion of Scampston Hall with its award-winning walled garden and holiday lodges (see 'Large country estates', page 22). Just to the south lies the small village of Thorpe Bassett.

■ **Malton and Norton-on-Derwent**
Lying about 5 miles (8 km) to the west of the trail, the market town of Malton and its neighbour Norton-on-Derwent straddle the River Derwent, the historic boundary between the North and East Ridings of Yorkshire. Malton has a long history and may be the site of the Roman settlement of Derventio. It had a Norman castle which was visited by Richard the Lionheart, Edward II and Robert the Bruce. There are many fine medieval buildings and Charles Dickens was a regular visitor; he may have written *A Christmas Carol* while staying here. The Catholic church of St Leonard and Mary

dates from the 12th century and is possibly the oldest church currently in use by Catholics in the country. Unfortunately the excellent Malton Museum, with its renowned collection of Roman artefacts, has now closed. The town has a wide range of independent shops and a regular market, while there are many places to stay and a good variety of pubs and restaurants. Malton now holds an annual food-lovers' festival in May, one of the best in Yorkshire.

An excellent trail leaflet describing a Malton Heritage Walk is available from the Tourist Information Centre in Malton.

Norton-on-Derwent, on the east bank of the River Derwent, is essentially part of the same community but there is a keen sense of local rivalry between Malton and Norton. Norton is more industrial, but is also famous for racehorse training.

■ **West Heslerton** This small village lies on the A64 main trunk road between Rillington and Sherburn. It has a pub, the Dawnay Arms, and a small church, All Saints, which is included on the Sykes Churches Trail (see page 94). It is also the site of a major archaeological survey into an extensive late Roman/early Anglo-Saxon settlement.

9 **East Heslerton** Also on the A64, East Heslerton has the wonderful St Andrew's Church with superb 105-foot (32-metre) octagonal spire, an attractive landmark from the trail as you approach Sherburn. This church is perhaps the most original of the churches on the Sykes Churches Trail (see page 94) and has survived thanks to the help of the Churches Conservation Fund. Nearby is evidence of an early medieval settlement.

Route description

To continue on the Yorkshire Wolds Way, leave **Thixendale 1** at the northern end of the main street **A** by walking up a track that cuts up the hillside to the right at an angle. Pass Cow Wold Barn on the right, go through a kissing-gate and keep to the track as it proceeds ahead along the field edge. Keep a look out for a sign where the route changes from one side of the hedge to the other. The change from the picturesque valley you have just left could not be more dramatic; the terrain here is of open fields, with buildings and hedges at a premium.

Descend steeply but briefly through two kissing-gates into Vessey Pasture Dale **B** and turn right and left to continue up the opposite bank, making sure that you keep the fence line on your right along the line of an ancient earthwork. At a path junction turn right **C** on to a fine green road that stretches ahead in a straight line for 1½ miles (2.4 km). At over 700 feet (213 metres), this is the highest point on the Way, with increasingly fine views northwards into Deep Dale. The fields here are almost prairie-like and it is tempting to assume that modern farming practices have

Thixendale to Sherburn

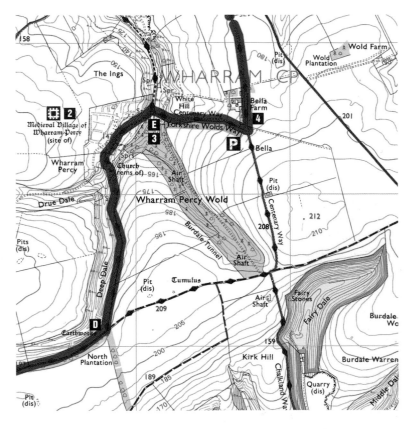

grubbed out hedges to create bigger cereal crops, but in fact medieval maps show that the field boundaries have not changed for centuries

Keep ahead through a field gate and at the eastern end of North Plantation **D** turn left to follow the gradually sloping path down to **Wharram Percy 2**, the deserted medieval settlement situated in one of the most beautiful and peaceful valleys you will find in the Yorkshire Wolds. On a fine, warm day you will be tempted to tarry longer than you planned, but when you finally have to leave, take the path past the ruined church down to the old railway track **E**. Close by is the 1,734-yard (1,586-

metre)-long Burdale Tunnel **3**, the longest railway tunnel in the Wolds. It was part of the Malton–Driffield railway line, known as 'The Dodger', which was opened in 1853 but closed in 1958. For decades it was the main link to the outside world for many Wolds residents and also carried thousands of tons of chalk from the nearby Wharram (also known as Burdale) Quarry, which is now a Yorkshire Wildlife Trust reserve famous for its orchids and butterflies.

The path crosses the railway trackbed and climbs gradually through several kissing-gates up to the small car park for visitors to Wharram Percy. Turn left down the road past Bella Farm **4** and,

One of the highlights of the Yorkshire Wolds Way, the deserted medieval village of Wharram Percy is a haven of tranquillity in an already secluded landscape.

where the road turns sharp right, continue ahead down the field side with the hedge on your right, then turn right along the road into the sleepy village of **Wharram le Street 5**.

At the crossroads, the route heads left, but a mile (1.6 km) ahead lies **Duggleby 6**, to which the energetic can detour to see the famous barrow known as Duggleby Howe (see 'The Yorkshire Wolds over the centuries', page 16).

Turn left along the B1248 – the main street of Wharram le Street – and at the end of the village go right **F** on the bridleway that heads up the hillside. As the route gradually climbs, extensive views open up to the north and west. Beyond the market town of Malton may be seen the **Howardian Hills**, separated from the moors by the Coxwold–Gilling Gap. To the north, across the flat Vale of Pickering, rise the slopes of the North York Moors

Cross the B1253 with care and keep straight ahead along the field edge on a track, turning left at a barn and continuing west as the path slopes down to a footbridge with gates at either end across Whitestone Beck. Go straight uphill and turn right along the farm road **G**, following it past Wood House and along the farm track towards Settrington Wood.

🚪 🚌 *To reach the village of* **North Grimston** *and the Middleton Arms pub, turn left along the farm road* **G** *and walk for about 1 mile (1.6 km) re-crossing the Whitestone Beck. When you emerge on to the busy and narrow B1248 road, turn right with care and the Middleton Arms will soon be found on your right-hand side.*

Where the track splits, go right and along the edge of the woodland. Where Wold Barn once stood **H**, the path turns sharp left and then right to proceed northwards again on a broad track, this time giving views to the west. This is

One of the largest round barrows in Britain, Duggleby Howe sits close to the Yorkshire Wolds Way near Wharram le Street.

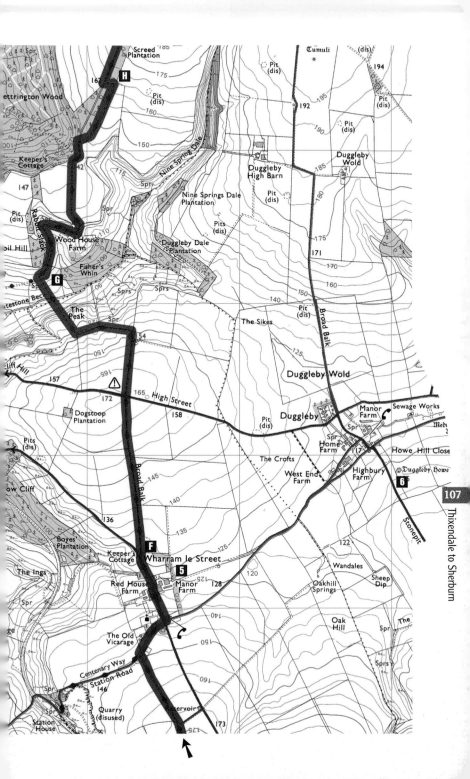

Cutting lavender by hand at Wolds Way Lavender near Wintringham.

The northern horizon is filled with the lumpy bulk of the North York Moors. Follow the clear path slanting down the hill and go straight on, reaching a metalled lane **J** that passes Rowgate Farm. After one mile (1.6 km), turn right at a small reservoir **K** and follow the bridleway along the edge of the first field. Cross the middle of the second field before crossing Wintringham Beck to reach the village.

🏠 🚌 ☕ *If planning an overnight stay around* **Malton**, *keep ahead on the metalled lane at* **K** *for ½ mile (800 metres). Keep ahead when you reach another lane and look out for a footpath on the left crossing a field diagonally towards* **Rillington**. *From Rillington there are bus connections to Malton, a large market town with a good range of facilities.*

When you reach the road in Wintringham, turn left and follow the road past the last house and then double back right along a rough lane **L** and through fields behind the village.

☕ *To visit Wolds Way Lavender with its huge range of lavender and herb beds and a tea room serving light refreshments (open April–October, but not every day; check details – see page 140), keep going left on the road for about ½ mile (800 metres), ignoring the next left-hand turn. You will find Wolds Way Lavender just beyond the junction on your left-hand side.*

enjoyable walking and the woods are good for spring flowers. Emerge from the trees to keep ahead past farm buildings to the road.

Cross the road **I** and follow the broad track into a small plantation that surrounds Beacon Wold, a service reservoir collecting water from a borehole into the chalk. The triangulation pillar on the left is on the 650-feet (198-metre) contour. Proceed through the wood on a path that forms a verdant tunnel in spring and summer as it curves to right and left. When you arrive at a gate, one of the most memorable views on the entire Yorkshire Wolds Way will be revealed. The escarpment tumbles down to **Wintringham** **7** and the Vale of Pickering is a patchwork of different shades of greens, browns and – when the oilseed rape is in season – yellows.

Follow the path towards St Peter's Church **8**, which, although usually locked, is still worth a detour. This is one of the most interesting churches on the trail and is rather big for a small village such as Wintringham.

Thixendale to Sherburn

The dramatic new art installation, Enclosure Rites, *on the trail at Knapton Plantation, north of Wintringham.*

Just after reaching the church, the route turns sharp left up the field side to enter Deep Dale Plantation. On entering the wood turn left on the forest track and, where it swings sharply to the left, turn sharp right up a thankfully short but very steep climb . Go through a gate and turn left, where you will soon arrive at the wonderful new art installation called *Enclosure Rites*, part of the 'Wander – Art on the Yorkshire Wolds Way' project, with its dramatic views out over the Vale of Pickering. Return to the trail to follow the old earthwork on a path enclosed by hedges until you reach a farm track. Turn left and

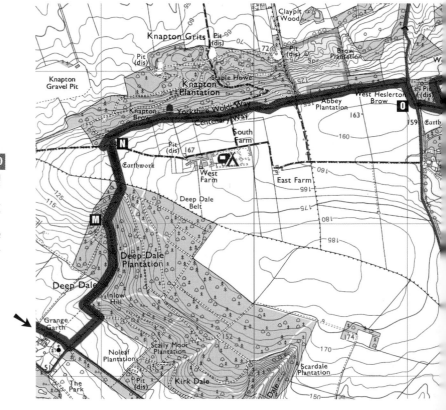

Thixendale to Sherburn

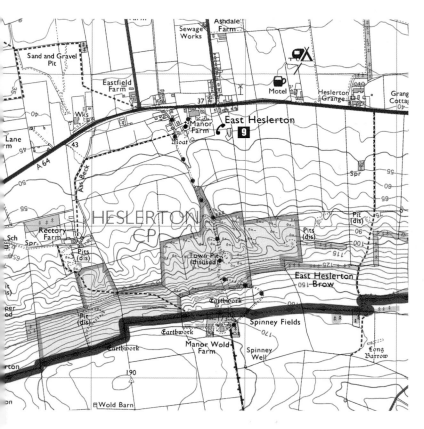

very soon right to enter the woods of Knapton Plantation **N**.

Alternatively, turn right if you are staying at the Yorkshire Wolds Way Caravan and Camping site. Usefully, the campsite has a shop which sells a few basic items.

From this point the north–south walking is virtually at an end; from now on, the primary direction will be west–east. This is West Heslerton Brow and at some points, in clear weather, you may catch your first glimpse of the North Sea. Keep on the track near the edge of the plantation; the alternative route from the caravan and campsite soon joins from the right. You emerge from the woods through a wooden kissing-gate and continue with

Abbey Plantation on your left. When you reach a lane **O**, detour round a small plantation masking an old pit and continue east with a fence on your left.

🍺 *The Dawnay Arms at* **West Heslerton** *is a 1-mile (1.6-km) detour to the left along the minor road. As you approach West Heslerton village, turn right into Church Street and the pub is at the next road junction on your right.*

There are fine views across **East Heslerton 9** and the Vale of Pickering from another of the attractive new benches installed along this section. Just after passing Manor Wold Farm the path crosses a minor lane and continues ahead over the fields.

Keep ahead and after several short ups and downs you reach a tarmac lane **P** and turn left. In a short distance look out for a signpost on the right which offers a field-edge path parallel to but above the road. This makes for easier and safer walking. Rejoin the road a little further on and continue down into Sherburn **10** 🚌, passing on your right the continuation of the Yorkshire Wolds Way to Filey.

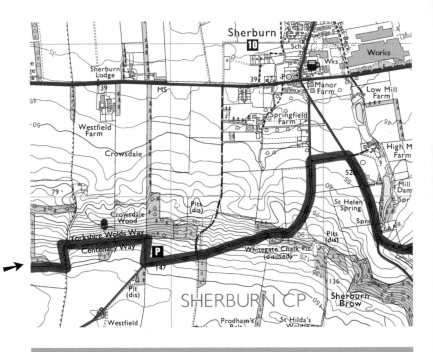

Public transport

Wharram le Street (on route) Postbus
North Grimston (1¼ miles/2 km) Postbus
Rillington (1¾ miles/2.8 km) 🚌
Malton (5 miles/8 km) 🚌
Wintringham (on route) 🚌 (twice weekly)
West Heslerton (¾ mile/1.2 km) 🚌
East Heslerton (1 mile/1.6 km) 🚌
Sherburn (¼ mile/400 metres) 🚌

Refreshments and toilets

North Grimston (1¼ miles/2 km) 🍺
Middleton Arms
Rillington (1¾ miles/2.8 km) 🍺 The
Fleece, Coach and Horses
Malton (5 miles/8 km) 🍺 ☕ good range
Wintringham (on route) ☕ Wolds Way
Lavender (limited opening)

West Heslerton (¾ mile/1.2 km) 🍺
Dawnay Arms
Food shops: Rillington, Malton
Public toilets: Malton

Accommodation

North Grimston (1¼ miles/2 km) Middleton
Arms (B&B), Hill Top Farm (camping)
Thorpe Bassett (¾ mile/1.2 km)
Old School House (B&B)
Norton (3¾ miles/6 km; north-east of
village) Brambling Fields (B&B)
Malton (5 miles/8 km) good range
West Knapton (alt. route) Yorkshire Wolds
Way Caravan and Camping
East Heslerton (1 mile/1.6 km)
Manor Farm House (B&B)

The interior of the ruined church of St Martin, Wharram Percy.

113

Fluxendale to Sherburn

The Yorkshire Wolds Way near East Heslerton and Staxton Wolds.

6 Sherburn to Filey

via Ganton and Muston
15 miles (24 km)

Ascent 1,621 feet (494 metres)
Descent 1,607 feet (490 metres)
Highest point Staxton Wold 581 feet (177 metres)
Lowest point Filey 38 feet (12 metres)

This final section takes you away from the Wolds and out of the countryside to meet the stunning chalk cliffs of the Yorkshire coast at your final destination, the bustling seaside resort of Filey. As a result, it may be tempting to put your head down to reach the coast, but there are some wonderful dry valleys and the wooded Stocking Dale to enjoy first, making this a final section to savour. When planning, please note that again there are few facilities en route. On your arrival in Filey, it is strongly recommended that you allow time to enjoy a walk along the only chalk sea cliffs in northern England, passing the superb bird reserve at Bempton Cliffs and Flamborough Head.

Things to look out for

1 Sherburn Located on the A64 trunk route, Sherburn is passed through by seemingly endless traffic heading to and from the coast. The main place of interest is St Hilda's Church, which is on the Sykes Churches Trail (see page 94) and contains 11 Saxon stone sculptures. Just to the south of the village lies Jackson's Wold Garden, a superb 3-acre (1.2-hectare) garden and nursery.

3 Ganton Another small village lying just off the busy A64 trunk route. The church of St Nicholas is a fine example of Early English and Perpendicular styles. Ganton Hall is a large 19th-century mansion and the seat of the Legard baronetcy, which dates back to 1660.

Ganton boasts a world-class golf course which has hosted amateur championships, the Ryder Cup in 1949 and the Walker Cup in 2003. On the main road, The Greyhound is a fine old coaching inn.

■ Staxton A small linear village at the foot of Staxton Hill, which is famous for its steep gradient and is notorious for accidents. This area has been inhabited by man since prehistoric times and nearby lies Starr Carr, one of the most important Mesolithic settlements in the country.

Staxton Wold RAF radar station was built on the top of Staxton Hill in 1937 and remains in use today. It is one of the oldest continually open radar stations in the country.

Just off the trail near Staxton Hill is the excellent Yorkshire Wolds Gallery and Tea Room.

7 Hunmanby The large village of Hunmanby lies to the south-west of Filey on the Centenary Way (see 'Other trails', page 31). The name has Danish origins, but there is evidence of earlier settlement. A British chariot burial site from the 1st or 2nd century BC was discovered here in 1907. Hunmanby still has its Market Place cross, which indicates its past importance in Yorkshire trade. There is a delightful 12th-century church and the original village lock-up can be found on Stonegate. The village has a good range of pubs and shops.

Just outside Hunmanby at Hunmanby Grange Farm is the Wolds Top Brewery, producing fine ales, including the special Wolds Way Ale that celebrates the National Trail. There is also an attractive garden on the working farm.

8 Muston This small village lies on the Yorkshire Wolds Way on the outskirts of Filey. The church of All Saints was rebuilt in the 19th century in Early English style. Muston has a pub called The Ship and is famous for its annual scarecrow festival.

9 Filey For many, Filey is the most attractive spot on the Yorkshire coast: a seaside town delightfully free of the worst excesses of holiday resorts, a magnificent bay well sheltered for bathing, windsurfing and yachting, with dramatic views of the chalk headland at Flamborough and Bempton in one direction and the great black finger of Filey Brigg in the other. Add the atmosphere of a traditional Yorkshire fishing village and its unique 'coble' boats, and you have a place of great charm.

Filey grew as a fishing community well before the Norman Conquest, and the fishing craft seen at the Coble Landing, flat-bottomed for beach-launching, have their roots in the Viking longboats that were a common sight on this coast more

With its French Victorian appearance, elegant Ganton Hall has been the seat of the Legard baronetcy for generations.

than a thousand years ago. They are used for line-fishing for white fish such as cod, haddock and plaice, and for the laying of 'fleets' of crab and lobster pots along the rocky shore.

The Georgian-style houses in The Crescent, overlooking the bay, were built in 1840 when Filey enjoyed brief prosperity as a spa town using mineral waters tapped on the cliffs above the Brigg. The most interesting part of town is in the Queen Street area. Look for the old house at the end of the street, close to the cliff edge, which was once called T'awd Ship Inn and was the haunt of smugglers.

13 Filey Brigg There is no geological curiosity on the English coast quite like Filey Brigg. At low tide the jagged reef, a ¾-mile (1.2-km) protrusion forming

an almost perfect right-angle to the bay, has the appearance of an aborted attempt at building a causeway across the North Sea. Thousands of years ago, a huge layer of clay was deposited on this coast by the action of glaciers, but it quickly eroded to expose a solid floor of lower calcareous gritstone that Scandinavian settlers named *bryggja*, meaning landing place.

It may look like a natural jetty on a calm summer's day, but the Brigg is carefully avoided by all craft, big and small, at any time of year. The coastal currents are fierce, onshore winds can be strong and many vessels have been shipwrecked on its black teeth. When the seas are high and visibility is poor, it must be considered out of bounds, and

The dramatic clay cliffs and long, rocky finger of Filey Brigg.

Scarborough's Grand Hotel and seafront.

walkers should always take care on the cliff in mist, high winds and, most important of all, at high tide.

The Brigg is very popular with birdwatchers, who see many rarities making landfall during the autumn and spring migration periods. Winter visitors that are frequently seen offshore include long-tailed ducks, red-throated divers and red-necked grebes. In the summer there are many gannets, kittiwakes and auks to be seen fishing nearby, as well as common and arctic terns. The cliff above the Brigg, known as Carr Nase, was the site of a Roman signal station, one of a series that stretched from Flamborough in the south to Scarborough, Ravenscar and beyond to the north. They performed an 'early warning' function, watching for a Viking invasion and preparing to relay the alarm by a series of beacons to Eboracum, the great Roman city that is now York.

■ **Scarborough** The largest of the seaside resorts on the Yorkshire coast, Scarborough lies about 8 miles (12.8 km) north of Filey. This spot has a long history of settlement dating back to the Stone and Bronze Ages, but with evidence of subsequent ransacking of these earlier places by the Vikings. A 12th-century castle was built on the rocky headland and the town grew steadily in the Middle Ages, based on its trading festivals immortalised in the song 'Scarborough Fair'.

Scarborough grew rapidly as a seaside resort with the arrival of the railways and the opening of the Grand Hotel in 1845; at the time it was one of the largest hotels in the world. The writer Anne Brontë died in the Grand Hotel in 1849 and is buried in St Mary's churchyard.

Scarborough has many attractions for the visitor, ranging from naval battle re-enactments in Peasholme Park, the annual literary festival and the Rotunda – one of the oldest purpose-built museums in the world, housing the William Smith Museum of Geology. In the 17th century mineral waters were discovered in the town and Scarborough developed as an elegant spa resort. By the 1960s, the mineral waters no longer flowed and the Spa was closed. However, the wonderful 19th-century buildings on the South Bay, designed by Joseph Paxton, have recently been refurbished and the Spa hosts the annual Scarborough Jazz Festival, one of the largest in Europe.

At the end of summer, cricket fans head for North Marine Road, where the annual Scarborough Cricket Festival takes place. This popular event features first class cricket and has been a highlight of the sporting calendar since 1876.

119

Gannets nesting at Bempton Cliffs.

■ Flamborough Head

Just a short distance along the coast from Bempton is Flamborough Head, one of the best-preserved chalk headlands in Britain. The breathtaking sea cliffs have been weathered to produce stacks, arches, blowholes and many caves. An interesting feature known as Danes Dyke is a ditch that runs from north to south and effectively cuts Flamborough Head off from the rest of Yorkshire. Despite the name, the dyke is prehistoric in origin. There are two lighthouses on the headland, one of which dates to the 17th century and is the oldest complete surviving lighthouse in the country. Flamborough Head has been the site of many shipwrecks, the most famous being the *Bonhomme Richard*, which sank in 1779. This was the flagship of the American John Paul Jones and was eventually sunk after one of the earliest actions by the US navy in the American Revolutionary War.

For a walk around Flamborough Head, see page 134.

Flamborough village, in the centre of the promontory, has some interesting old buildings, including the 12th-century church of St Oswald and the remains of the fortified Flamborough Manor.

■ Bempton Cliffs RSPB Reserve

Located just to the south-east of Filey, the towering 400-foot (122-metre) chalk cliffs of Bempton are an essential place to visit for any Yorkshire Wolds Way walker. These cliffs are a continuation of the same line of chalk that you have been following since the Humber Estuary and part of the only northern chalk cliffs in Britain. The RSPB reserve is home to 200,000 nesting birds during the breeding months and is one of the best places in the country to get close to sea birds. Puffins can be seen between April and July, while Bempton has the biggest mainland colony of gannets in the country. Other species which can be spotted here include guillemots, razorbills, kittiwakes and fulmar. See also 'Wildlife of the Yorkshire Wolds', page 24.

■ Bridlington

Below Flamborough Head lies Bridlington, a classic traditional English seaside resort with fine sandy beaches, a bustling harbour and an atmospheric old town. The site has been settled since the Bronze Age and may have been the site of a Roman station, as Woldgate, a Roman road, heads west from Bridlington towards York. The town grew in importance due to the fishing industry and development as a popular seaside resort in the 19th century.

Bridlington has developed over the years in two distinct areas around its old town and commercial centre inland and the harbour and traditional holiday resort on the coast. A circular walk on page 130 explores both parts of this fascinating town. The old heart of Bridlington can also be explored following *The Old Town Trail* walking guide available at the local Tourist Information Centre. Highlights include the Market Place complete with stocks, the Corn Exchange and the Priory, which once outshone Beverley Minster before its destruction during the Reformation. The surviving nave remains as a mighty building and the pair of towers added in the 19th century enclose one of the largest Perpendicular windows in Yorkshire. The very popular Bayle Museum is housed in what was once the gatehouse to the Priory.

There is a thriving arts culture in this town where David Hockney is based, with many galleries showing the works of a growing and talented range of artists.

Bridlington Quay, which contains the working harbour, is a bustling, vibrant place. This is one of the most important shellfish ports in the country with a lucrative export market to the continent.

Just outside the town lies Sewerby Hall, an elegant Georgian mansion and gardens with a collection of memorabilia from Amy Johnson, the Hull-born aviation pioneer.

■ **Rudston Monolith** The Rudston Monolith is the tallest megalith or standing stone in the country. It is located in the churchyard of All Saints, Rudston, and stands at 25 feet (7.6 metres) high. Its location pre-dates the Norman church and it could have been

erected as long as go as 1600 BC. The author Winifred Holtby (see page 27) was born in the village and is buried in the churchyard. Rudston is about 5 miles (8 km) to the west of Bridlington.

■ **Burton Agnes** Also to be found in the countryside about 6 miles (9.6 km) south-west of Bridlington is the ensemble of buildings that make up Burton Agnes. There is a magnificent Elizabethan manor house which was built by Sir William Griffith in the early 1600s and was the seat of the baronetcy of Boynton for many years. One of the finest country houses in England, Burton Agnes is now owned by a trust fund. The hall and the nearby manor house are open to the public and the superb gardens boast 3,000 flower species, including the national collection of campanulas. The display of snowdrops on the woodland walk can be stunning in late winter.

The church of St Martin is approached through a dense tunnel of yew trees and has some unusual tombs of members of the Griffith family.

■ **Kilham and Woldgate** Between Rudston and Burton Agnes to the west of Bridlington, the Roman road known as Woldgate leads directly to the large village of Kilham. Kilham was once a thriving market town greater in importance than Driffield, but it declined when a canal link to Driffield was established. The Norman church of All Saints hosts an annual flower festival and has an unusual weathervane in the shape of a turkey. The village boasts a range of local businesses and a thriving artistic community. David Hockney has painted many pictures along Woldgate and around Kilham, including his famous tunnel of trees through the seasons.

Route description

Leave **Sherburn 1** by heading south from the main street, and rejoin the route by going back up the right fork of the road and taking the left turning through a field. At the far end turn right **A** on the tarmac lane leading to Butterwick, Foxholes and Weaverthorpe. High Mill, passed on the left, was a fine water-powered mill until well into the 20th century. Take great care, as the traffic is fast moving along this road.

Fork left steeply up the lane **B** and in a short distance bear left along the field edge, following the contour of the hill through scrub woodland. After a sharp right turn uphill, turn left to follow a pleasant path into woodland. After only a short distance this path swings downhill and back into the fields. After passing two fields on your right, turn

sharp right **C** and follow the sandy track past Manor Farm to a lane.

☕ *To reach the Sally Middlewood Farm bakery and tea room at Potter Brompton, turn left along the track at Manor Farm and walk for ¼ mile (400 metres). You will find the tea room on the right on the A64. It is open daily except Christmas Day, Boxing Day and New Year's Day.*

After turning briefly right then left, continue along a limestone track to the next tarmac lane. Ganton Hall **2**, which is glimpsed through the trees farther up the hill, is Victorian and is often likened to a French château. Turn left down the lane towards peaceful **Ganton 3**, with its whitewashed houses and stream gurgling alongside the road.

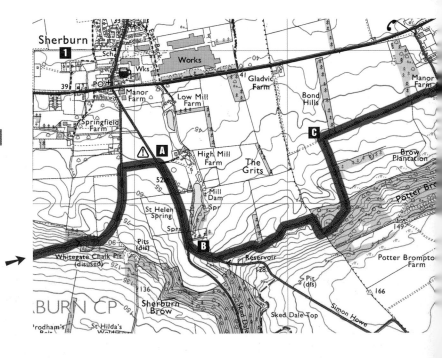

Keep ahead on the road through Ganton for ¼ mile (400 metres) to reach the A64 road junction and a restaurant/bar called the Ganton Greyhound.

Turn right along Main Street and at the bend continue ahead, with views of the magnificent 14th-century spire of St Nicholas Church on the left **4**. Keep ahead along the field edge with the hedge on your right. At the narrow plantation **D** turn sharp right up the hill. Turn left and then right up a sunken lane along an avenue of gnarled old trees, continuing uphill turning left, right and left again to reach the busy B1249.

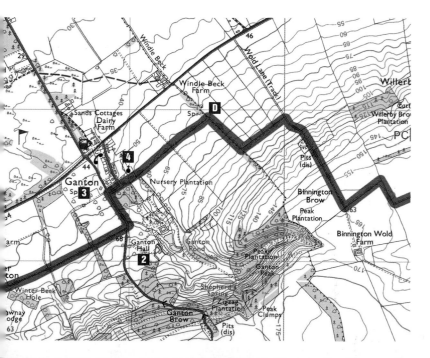

The 18th-century coaching inn at Ganton.

A short distance to the left is the popular Willerby Brow picnic spot with superb views and public toilets.

☕ *About 1 mile (1.6 km) along the road to the right is the Yorkshire Wolds Gallery and Tea Room, which has limited opening times (see page 140).*

Take care crossing the road and continue ahead along the track past Grange Farm, with first a plantation and then open fields on your left. This is a private road but also a public footpath, which continues for about a mile (1.6 km) before turning right to pass the buildings and mast of RAF Staxton Wold **5**.

🚏 *Turn left here along Wold Lane for about ¾ mile (1.2 km) to reach the village of **Staxton**. At the A64 turn left*

along the wider verge opposite and the Hare and Hounds pub is located a short distance away on the right-hand side.

After turning right and passing the RAF base, continue downhill past High Farm as the track deteriorates into a sunken path. When it begins to level out look out for the footpath on the left which climbs steeply uphill **E** out of the dale through two kissing-gates on to an open landscape, keeping the boundary on your left. You are now in a wonderful but demanding section of the trail, as the path keeps straight ahead apart from one short dog-leg, ascending and descending through magnificent and rugged countryside. You cross the heads of two small dry valleys before climbing steeply to reach a tarmac road **F**.

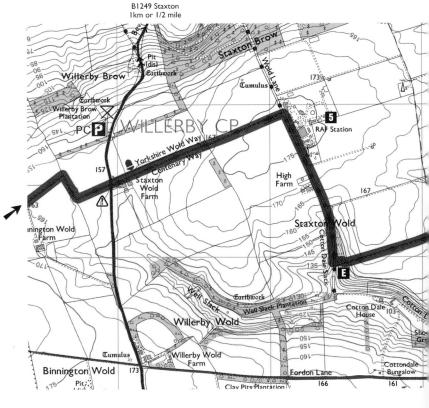

B1249 Staxton
1km or 1/2 mile

Turn left here and follow the road for about a mile (1.6 km) as it drops steadily towards the A1039 trunk road. Flixton village and the pub the Fox Hound is a short distance along the main road to your right. The campsite at Humble Bee Farm is located to the left off this minor lane.

To continue on the Yorkshire Wolds Way, turn right for about 350 yards (320 metres), then left to follow the field-edge path above Raven Dale. Go right as the path curves around the head of Camp Dale **G** before finally dropping downhill to

The village green at Muston.

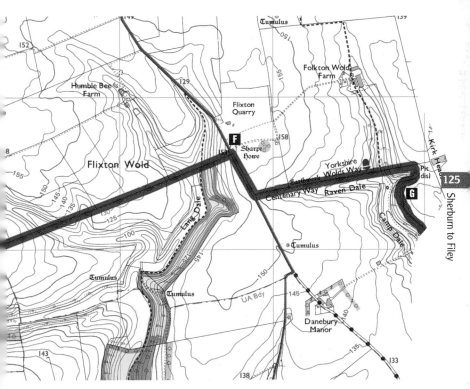

The Camp **6**, which lies at the junction of Camp Dale and Stocking Dale and is the site of one of the many deserted medieval villages to be found in the Yorkshire Wolds (see page 19). Little can be seen today apart from an old dew pond and some grassed-over mounds.

The Yorkshire Wolds Way now turns left up Stocking Dale, which is a peaceful and attractively wooded dale.

For an alternative route into Filey, turn right at The Camp and follow the Centenary Way down the valley via the village of **Hunmanby 7 🚏 🚌** to Filey.

To stay on the main route, follow the track up Stocking Dale and out into open fields before turning right on to a farm track, passing a small plantation and Stockendale Farm. Cross the busy road with care and continue ahead along the

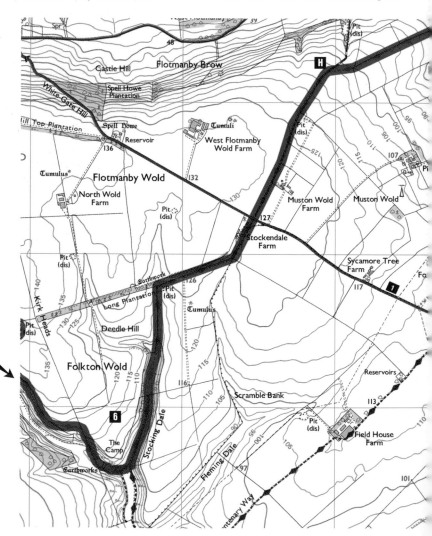

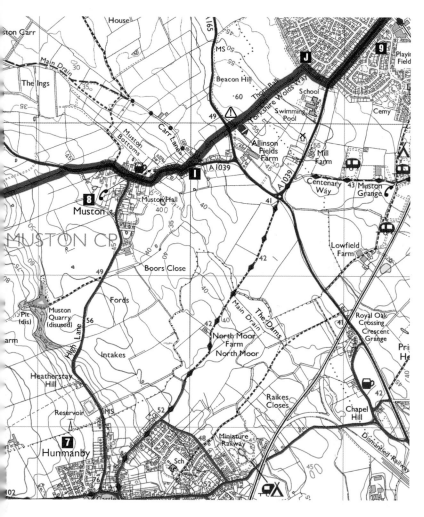

field-edge track, then after about ¾ mile (1.2 km) look carefully for the sign to bear right , following a cross-field path to a kissing-gate in the hedge on the far side of the field. With a hedge on your left, the field path now descends the chalk scarp through two kissing-gates towards **Muston 8**, with good views to the right towards the chalk cliffs of Speeton and Bempton. Turn right to follow the main road through Muston, passing the ⬛ Ship Inn on your left.

Just before the end of the village a short loop road on the left gives access to a path on the right of a terrace of houses ⬛; from here cross two fields and then the main A165 Scarborough–Bridlington road with care.

Keep ahead through the field and walk down towards the school playing field, then turn right ⬛ over a sleeper bridge to meet the main road into **Filey 9** ⬛ ☕ 🚌 🚆.

You now have a choice, as there are several ways of passing through Filey to reach the end of the Yorkshire Wolds Way. The official route turns left along the main road into the town and goes straight ahead after passing the bus station to drop steeply downhill to the shore.

However, the quickest way to reach the sea is to turn left then almost immediately right down Grange Avenue, swinging right along Clarence Drive. Pass under the railway and continue ahead to the seafront.

At the foot of Church Ravine **10** a flight of steps opposite the toilets leads up on to the cliff top, from where you can make your way through the Country Park **11** to the sculpture which marks the end of the Yorkshire Wolds Way and also the Cleveland Way. If the tide is low, an attractive alternative route passes the lifeboat station and follows the beach beneath Pampletine Cliffs **12** and along the rocks towards **Filey Brigg 13**. A path ascends the cliff a short distance before the clay cliff terminates, and once on the cliff top it is only a short distance back to the sculpture. From near here there are

magnificent views northwards towards **Scarborough** and Robin Hood's Bay, and to the south, beyond the wide sweep of Filey Bay, rise the dramatic chalk cliffs of **Bempton**.

If you wish to explore Filey Brigg please take care and make sure you check on the tide times (see page 138) before venturing out on to the narrow peninsula.

Congratulations! All walkers who complete the Yorkshire Wolds Way are invited to visit the Tourist Information Centre in Filey or the Country Park Stores at Filey Country Park to enter their comments in the special book.

If you have some time to spare, I would strongly recommend that you either walk or take the Bridlington bus as far as Speeton, then take the Headland Way through the church car park and over fields to follow the coast path along these magnificent chalk cliffs to a grand finish at Flamborough Head – surely a fitting climax to your walk along the backbone of the Yorkshire Wolds. You can even continue the walk around the southern side of Flamborough Head to arrive in **Bridlington** on foot. (See also Flamborough Head Walk, page 134.)

Bridlington's imposing Town Hall was opened in 1932.

Public transport

Ganton (¼ mile/400 metres) 🚌
Hunmanby (1¼ miles/ 2 km) 🚌
Muston (on route) 🚌
Filey (on route) 🚆 🚌
Taxis: Filey

Refreshments and toilets

Potter Brompton (¼ mile/ 400 metres) 🍺 Sally Middlewood
Ganton (¼ mile/400 metres) 🍺 Ganton Greyhound (limited opening)
Staxton (¾ mile/1.2 km) 🍺 Hare and Hounds, (restaurant) Harpers
Flixton (1 mile/1.6 km) 🍺 Foxhound Inn
Muston (on route) 🍺 Ship Inn
Hunmanby (1¼ miles/ 2 km) 🍺 Cottage Inn, Royal Oak, Wrangham House Hotel
Filey (on route) 🍺, restaurants: wide range
Food shops: Hunmanby, Filey
Public toilets: Filey, Staxton Wold

Accommodation

Weaverthorpe (3 miles/ 4.8 km) Bluebell Inn, Star Inn (B&B)
Ganton (¼ mile/ 400 metres) Ganton Greyhound (inn),
Windlebeck Farm (camping)
Foxholes (2¾ miles/ 4.4 km) Manor Farmhouse (B&B)
Langtoft (5 miles/8 km) Old Mill Hotel (hotel)
Wold Newton (3½ miles/ 5.6 km) Wold Cottage (B&B, camping)
Flixton (1 mile/1.6 km) (Orchard Lodge (B&B), Humble Bee Farm (camping)
Hunmanby (1¼ miles/ 2 km) Asperoy (B&B), The Southgate (B&B), Royal Oak (B&B), Wrangham House Hotel
Filey (on route) wide range

Bridlington Old Town and Quay Walk

This 5-mile (8-km) circular walk starts and finishes at Bridlington railway station. The described route heads first towards the coast, but this walk can easily be done in the other direction, taking in the old town first. Allow plenty of time to explore the Old Town with its interesting shops, galleries, cafés and the harbour area.

Leave the station and walk along Station Approach Road with a large Tesco on your right. Looking over to your left you will see the prominent dome of the **Town Hall**. Turn right on to the Scarborough Road, then first right into Springfield Avenue. At the end of the road turn right into Hilderthorpe Road, then second left into Windsor Crescent. You are now amongst the tight terraced housing of Bridlington, with a plethora of holiday accommodation.

As the road divides, take the left fork, still on Windsor Crescent, and head downhill towards the bay. Before the end of the road turn right into Thorpe Street and immediately left into Albert Street. At the end of the road turn right into West Street, passing the Spotlight Theatre on your right, and take the second on the left, Neptune Street, which leads towards the sea front with the large art-deco building **The Spa** directly ahead. Look out on the right for the **Lifeboat House**, which was built in 1903, and the magnificent sandy **South Beach** off the promenade to your right.

Turn left on to the main road in front of The Spa, with the recently refurbished Pembroke Gardens on your left.

Bridlington's bustling **harbour** soon appears below on your right. With its many colourful fishing boats, piles of

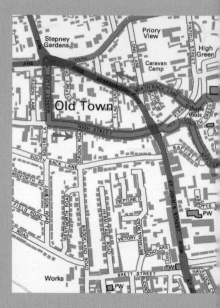

lobster pots and noisy gulls overhead, this is a fascinating place to linger. Bridlington is one of the busiest shellfish ports in the country, so there is always plenty of activity around the harbour.

On the left, in front of an incongruously large tower block, are **South Cliff Gardens** with their distinctive line of flagpoles. Look out for a sundial memorial to Lawrence of Arabia, who served in the RAF at Bridlington between 1929 and 1935.

At a pelican crossing by the gardens look for a set of bollards on your right leading to an elevated walkway above the harbour area, with excellent views south along the coast towards Hornsea. Head along this walkway to the end, then down the steps on the left to a car park below. Go straight ahead towards the steep bank beyond the car park, then right through a gap in the railings. You now have the harbour on your right and the buildings of Queen Street above you. Keep ahead into Harbour Road at the heart of the

BRIDLINGTON

Bridlington Quay area, passing the **Harbour Heritage Museum** on your left. Entry to this fascinating little museum, which is run by the Sailing Coble Preservation Society, is free and it is full of maritime memorabilia. A 'coble' is an old sailing vessel, one of which, *The Three Brothers*, celebrated its centenary in 2013 and can be seen moored in the harbour.

Just beyond the museum and before a building with a cannon on the top, climb a flight of steps to your left. You emerge at the end of Prince Street with the Tourist Information Centre a short way down to the left. Turn to the right, then left to follow the promenade heading up the **North Beach**. There are excellent views along the coast towards Sewerby and **Flamborough Head**, with the lighthouse visible on clear days.

Walk past the long line of amusements and the **Pavilion**, then where the promenade turns inland descend steps to continue ahead on another walkway, called Victoria Terrace, to pass the Leisure World complex. Keep heading north on what is now called Beaconsfield Promenade, looking out for a church spire which can be seen to your left behind the terraced houses of Albion Terrace and Bright Crescent.

A flight of steps on your right leads down to the beach, where you can turn immediately inland under a metal bridge dated 1888 and up a tarmac path under another bridge towards the church. This narrow defile is known as **Trinity Cut** and was a lifeboat slipway in the days when horses were used.

If the tide is high or the sea is rough, avoid the beach by taking the path on your left just beyond the old metal bridge; this will bring you to Trinity Cut.

Walk past **Holy Trinity Church**, dating from 1871, and turn half-right on to the busy Flamborough Road, passing a long row of B&B establishments and going under a railway bridge. Beyond the bridge turn half-left on the diagonal path across **Queens Park**. At the end of the park cross the dual carriageway, Queensgate, and enter St Oswalds Road directly opposite. Turn left into Priory Crescent and take the footpath located between house numbers 35 and 37. Continue on this footpath as it crosses St Aiden's Road and passes through **Bridlington Cemetery** with its attractive chapel, before emerging on Priory Walk with Bridlington Priory Church visible ahead.

Keep ahead on Priory Walk, then turn right and left on a footpath, passing allotments and the magnificent Bridlington Priory Church on your right, to come out on the Church Green – an attractive open area with the Bayle Gate Museum on your left.

In 2013, at the time of writing, the **Priory Church of St Mary**, Bridlington is celebrating its 900th birthday, having been founded in 1113 as a house of Augustinian canons. It grew in importance to become second only to York in the county. Its last prior joined the Pilgrimage of Grace protests (see page 31), after which the priory was partly destroyed and all its assets seized. The huge nave was spared to be passed to the parish and effectively become the church we see today.

Walk towards the museum, but turn right across Kirkgate into North Back Lane. At the end of the road turn right on the main Scarborough Road, then second left into Market Place in the Old Town. Look out for the **Corn Exchange** building on your left and the old **stocks and pillory** outside the Pack Horse before turning left into the High Street.

You are now in the heart of the **Old Town**, with the street lined on both sides with superb old houses and shops dating mainly from the 17th and 18th centuries. Look out on the left for number 64A, which until recently was an old-fashioned chemist's shop, and for the large convent building further along on the same side. There is a wonderful range of eclectic shops, galleries and cafés along the High Street where you may wish to linger.

At the end of High Street re-cross Scarborough Road and walk back towards the **Bayle Gate**. This was built originally as a gateway to the priory and survived the destruction during the Reformation because it was being used as a courthouse to the manor. It now houses an interesting museum of the history of Bridlington. (It is open from Easter to September, Monday–Friday, 11 a.m.–4 p.m.)

Just before the priory turn right down Applegarth Lane, passing on your right the tiny chapel and the grave of Robert Prudon, who founded the first Baptist congregation here and died in 1708. Turn right into St Mary's Walk, continuing past the big new East Riding College.

Cross Queensgate and enter St Thomas Road, passing a park on your right. At the end of the park take the tarmac footpath on the right that runs parallel to the park behind houses. Keep ahead past a range of sports facilities and cross the railway through two gates over the tracks. Turn right on Victoria Road, noting **Field House** on your left, which was built over a spring as a country house in the early 1800s. At the end you will meet the main Scarborough Road again. Turn right, then left to retrace your steps to the station.

A Flamborough Head Walk

This magnificent 7½-mile (12-km) coastal walk around Flamborough Head starts and finishes in Flamborough village, which can be reached by bus 150 from Bridlington Bus Station (not Sundays). The walk is hilly in parts, with a very steep descent and climb at South Landing. There are cafés at Thornwick Bay, North Landing and Flamborough Head but few facilities beyond there. Please note that these cliffs can be dangerous and this part of the English coastline suffers greatly from coastal erosion. Don't venture too close to the edge and please observe any diversion or closure notices.

From the bus stop outside the **Tuck Shop** and the **Royal Dog and Duck Inn** on Tower Street, walk towards the roundabout and take the road opposite signed towards North Landing and Thornwick Bay. As the road bends to the right, take the footpath on your left signed North Cliff 1¼ miles, going through a wooden kissing-gate and following the hedge line on your left.

Pass through a second wooden kissing-gate and follow a short section of fenced path before turning right at a path junction. You now enter a huge field with the boundary on your right-hand side. Keep on this path as a complex of holiday homes appears over the hedge on the right with occasional sea views. This is easy walking, to the sound of skylarks in spring. At the end of the field follow the same general line on a more enclosed path which can be muddy underfoot in wet weather.

You now enter another large field and keep ahead, with views to the south-east opening up along the coast towards

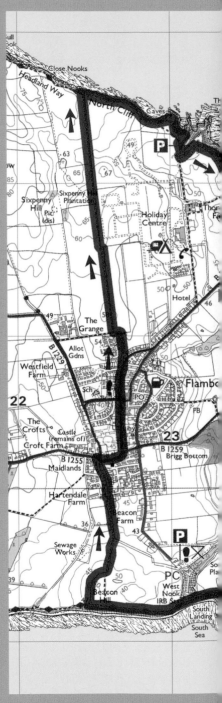

East Scar

Caves

Carter Lane

Breil Nook

The Sad

North Marine
Estate

Breil Head

Cradle Head

North Moor

BOROUGH CP

Stottle Bank
Nook

Flatmere
Plantation

Selwicks Bay

**Flamborough
Head**

Green Acre
Caravan Park

CH

Tower

52

52

Cough
Hole

B1259

Lighthouse Road

ingley Hills

24

Starling Hill

Station

26

Ocean View
Farm

25

Head Farm

48

High
Stacks

Old Fall
Plantation

Cattlemere Hole

Cross Bow
Hill

Tumulus

Old Fa

Headland Way

Cattlemere Scar

Cliffe House
Farm

New Fa

Craike

Mean High Water

South Cliff

Mean Low Water

Two
Stones

eat Scars

Flamborough Head. Climb the slight incline at the end of the field and you find yourself on the coast path, with superb views west towards Bempton and Filey and east towards Thornwick Bay and North Landing.

Turn right on to the Headland Way (see 'Other trails', page 31), which you will follow for the greater part of this circular walk. For walkers who have completed the Yorkshire Wolds Way to Filey, this is the final part of their walk along this magnificent northern chalk ridge.

Towards Thornwick Bay the route heads inland through a brand-new wooden kissing-gate into a fenced area where the Yorkshire Wildlife Trust are grazing sheep. The footpath now takes you further away from the coast and out of the sheep-grazing area through another new kissing-gate. Turn left on a permissive path – part of the Flamborough Heritage Trail – towards a white building and along a wide track which takes you past **Thornwick Bay**. The white building is the Thornwick Bay Café which has seasonal opening hours. When you reach a path/road junction turn left towards the coast. Don't take the path that goes down a gully into the bay, but head along the grass verge, aiming to the left of the cottages ahead. You will soon be back on the coast path, passing behind these cottages with superb views north-west back towards the towering cliffs of Bempton.

The path descends steeply into a gully and rises again, crossing a small bridge before reaching the picturesque bay of **North Landing** with its tiny, steep landing stage. Here you meet the road from Flamborough, and there is a large car park. There are also useful public toilets and a café which is open daily between 9.30 a.m. and 4 p.m. from May to September.

Walk past the café and pick up the Headland Way again, following the sign marked Lighthouse 1¾ miles. Climbing steps, this route winds superbly around the eastern side of North Landing, affording further tremendous views back along the coast. Follow the signs and keep the fence line on your right along this indented coastline. Look out for the superb sea stack

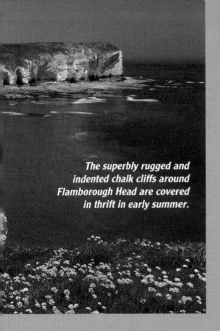

The superbly rugged and indented chalk cliffs around Flamborough Head are covered in thrift in early summer.

in a bay which is a haven for seabirds. After a fenced section you pass a path to the **North Cliff Marsh Nature Reserve** on your right, then some farmland followed by the golf course, which is perched precariously on the cliff edge.

There are great views of both the **old and new lighthouses** on the approach to Flamborough Head. The path descends through scrubland and turns right on a track towards the Cliff End Café. For more on Flamborough Head, see page 120.

Turn left at the road and walk towards the lighthouse past a long row of memorial benches and the Headlands Restaurant. Pass beside the lighthouse and aim ahead towards the Fog Repeater Station on the cliff edge along a tarmac path.

Before the coast, turn right on the footpath, following the Headland Way towards South Landing 2½ miles (4 km) away on an indistinct path over grassland. Where you come to a junction of routes, follow the left-hand path along the coast to enter open farmland with views of both lighthouses beyond. The cliffs here seem

less incised than on the northern side of Flamborough Head and there are also excellent views back towards Bridlington and Holderness beyond.

Continue to follow the Headland Way through arable fields and beyond a junction of paths. The route cuts inland on flights of steps around a series of narrow gullies. Finally the path heads inland towards **South Landing**. Join a wide track near a sculptured bench and a memorial to St Oswald, patron saint of fishermen – part of the South Landing Sculpture Trail. Keep ahead on this fenced path to descend a long, steep flight of steps into South Landing. This is an attractive small bay with an RNLI shop.

Turn left past the shop, then right up a very steep flight of steps to the top of the cliffs and open fields. There are more excellent views southwards to Danes Dyke, Sewerby and Bridlington before you leave the coast at the next path junction. Turn right on a footpath signed Flamborough ½ mile and follow the path round the field edge with the church tower ahead. At the end of the field go through the gate and keep ahead on a wide track. Climb the stile beside the next gate and go through Beacon Farm.

Beyond the farm you emerge into **Flamborough village**. Aiming for the church, keep ahead on West Street, which turns into Butlers Lane. Turn left into Lily Lane and right again into West Street. At the end turn right on to Church Street and on your right pass the attractive **church of St Oswald** with its unusual weathervane. Turn next left into Tower Street, passing the remains of **Flamborough Castle**, a medieval fortified manor house in the field on your left, before arriving back at the start outside the **Tuck Shop**.

PART THREE
Useful Information

Contact details

Yorkshire Wolds Way National Trail Office

c/o North York Moors National Park, The Old Vicarage, Bondgate, Helmsley, York, North Yorkshire YO62 5BP

ⓘ www.nationaltrail.co.uk/yorkshirewoldsway
✎ m.hodgson@northyorkmoors.org.uk
☎ 01439 770657

National Trails Office at Natural England

ⓘ www.nationaltrail.co.uk
✎ national.trail@naturalengland.org.uk

East Riding of Yorkshire Council

ⓘ www.eastriding.gov.uk
online fault-reporting form for the route
✎ customer.services@eastriding.gov.uk
☎ 01482 393939
Responsible for the trail between Hessle and Fridaythorpe.

North Yorkshire County Council

ⓘ www.northyorks.gov.uk
✎ paths@northyorks.gov.uk
☎ 0845 872 7374
Responsible for the trail between Fridaythorpe and Filey.

Tide Times

ⓘ www.tidetimes.org.uk

Travel information

National Rail Enquiries

ⓘ www.nationalrail.co.uk
☎ 0845 748 4950

Traveline Yorkshire

ⓘ www.yorkshiretravel.net
☎ 0871 200 2233

Hull Trains

ⓘ www.hulltrains.co.uk
☎ 0845 071 0222

Northern Rail

ⓘ www.northernrail.org
☎ 0845 000 0125

TransPennine Express

ⓘ www.tpexpress.co.uk
☎ 0845 600 1671

Grand Central Trains

ⓘ www.grandcentralrail.com
☎ 0844 811 0071

National Express Coaches

ⓘ www.nationalexpress.com
☎ 08717 818178

East Yorkshire Bus Company

ⓘ www.eyms.co.uk
☎ 01482 222222

P&O Ferries

ⓘ www.poferries.com
☎ 0871 664 2020

Accommodation

A full downloadable accommodation guide is available from the Yorkshire Wolds Way National Trail website.

Tourist information

Visit England

ⓘ www.visitengland.org

Visit Hull and East Yorkshire

ⓘ www.visithullandeastyorkshire.com
☎ 01482 486600

Hull Tourist Information Centre

☎ 01482 223559
✎ tourist.information@hullcc.gov.uk

Humber Bridge Tourist Information Centre

☎ 01482 640852
✎ humberbridge.tic@eastriding.gov.uk

Beverley Tourist Information Centre
☎ 01482 391672
✉ beverley.tic@eastriding.gov.uk

York Visitor Information Centre
ⓘ www.visityork.org
☎ 01904 550099
✉ info@visityork.org

Malton Tourist Information Centre
☎ 01653 600048
✉ maltontic@btconnect.com

Filey Tourist Information Centre
☎ 01723 383637
✉ tourism.bureau@scarborough.gov.uk

Bridlington Tourist Information Centre
☎ 01262 673474
✉ Bridlington.tic@eastriding.gov.uk

Scarborough Tourist Information Centre
☎ 01723 383637
✉ scarboroughtic@scarborough.gov.uk

Walking holiday providers for the Yorkshire Wolds Way

Brigantes
ⓘ www.brigantesenglishwalks.com
✉ mike@brigantesenglishwalks.com
☎ 01756 770402

Contours Walking Holidays
ⓘ www.contours.co.uk
✉ info@contours.co.uk
☎ 01629 821900

Discovery Travel
ⓘ www.discoverytravel.co.uk
✉ info@discoverytravel.co.uk
☎ 01904 632226

Macs Adventure Holidays
ⓘ www.macsadventure.com
✉ info@macsadventure.com
☎ 0141 530 8886

Other contacts

Burnby Hall Gardens
ⓘ www.burnbyhallgardens.com
✉ info@burnbyhallgardens.com
☎ 01759 307125

Burton Agnes Hall and Gardens
ⓘ www.burtonagnes.com
✉ office@burtonagnes.com
☎ 01262 490324

Churches Conservation Trust
ⓘ www.visitchurches.org.uk
✉ central@thecct.org.uk
☎ 0845 303 2760

East Yorkshire Historic Churches Trust (Sykes Churches Trail)
ⓘ www.eychurches.org.uk

English Heritage
ⓘ www.english-heritage.org.uk
✉ customers@english-heritage.org.uk
☎ 0870 333 1181

Environment Agency
ⓘ www.environment-agency.gov.uk
✉ enquiries@environment-agency.gov.uk
☎ 0370 850 6506

Hockney Trail – art locations in the Wolds
ⓘ www.yocc.co.uk

Howardian Hills AONB
ⓘ www.howardianhills.org.uk
✉ info@howardianhills.org.uk
☎ 0845 034 9495

Hull History Centre
ⓘ www.hullhistorycentre.org.uk
✉ hullhistorycentre@hullcc.gov.uk
☎ 01482 317500

Hull Museums and Galleries
ⓘ www.hullcc.gov.uk/museums
✉ info@hullcc.gov.uk
☎ 01482 300300

Long Distance Walkers Association
ⓘ www.ldwa.org.uk

Useful Information

Madhyamaka Buddhist Centre Kilnwick Percy
- (i) www.madhyamaka.org
- ✎ info@madhyamaka.org
- ☎ 01759 304832

National Trust
- (i) www.nationaltrust.org.uk
- ✎ enquiries@nationaltrust.org.uk
- ☎ 0844 800 1895

Open Spaces Society
- (i) www.oss.org.uk
- ✎ hq@oss.org.uk
- ☎ 01491 573535

Ordnance Survey
- (i) www.ordnancesurvey.co.uk
- ✎ customerservices@ordnancesurvey.co.uk
- ☎ 0845 605 0505

Philip Larkin Society
- (i) www.philiplarkin.com

The Ramblers
- (i) www.ramblers.org.uk
- ✎ ramblers@ramblers.org.uk
- ☎ 0207 339 8500

Robert Fuller Gallery
- (i) www.robertfuller.com
- ✎ mail@robertfuller.com
- ☎ 01759 368355

Royal Society for the Protection of Birds (RSPB)
- (i) www.rspb.org.uk
- ☎ 01767 680551

Scampston Hall and Gardens
- (i) www.scampston.co.uk
- ✎ info@scampston.co.uk
- ☎ 01944 759111

Sledmere House and Gardens
- (i) www.sledmerehouse.com
- ✎ info@sledmerehouse.com
- ☎ 01377 236637

Sustrans
- (i) www.sustrans.org.uk
- ✎ info@sustrans.org.uk
- ☎ 0845 113 0065

Wold Top Brewery
- (i) www.woldtopbrewery.co.uk
- ✎ enquiries@woldtopbrewery.co.uk
- ☎ 01723 892222

Wolds Way Lavender
- (i) www.woldswaylavender.com

Woodland Trust
- (i) www.woodlandtrust.org.uk
- ✎ enquiries@woodlandtrust.org.uk
- ☎ 01476 581135

Yorkshire Nature Triangle
- (i) www.yorkshirenaturetriangle.com
- ✎ nature.triangle@ywt.org.uk

Yorkshire Wildlife Trust
- (i) www.ywt.org.uk
- ✎ info@ywt.org.uk
- ☎ 01904 659570

Yorkshire Wolds Heritage Trust
- (i) www.yorkshirewoldsheritage.org.uk
- ✎ mail@yorkshirewoldsheritage.org.uk

Yorkshire Wolds Heritage Centre
- ✎ roseandrobin@vistaarts.co.uk
- ☎ 01377 219135

Yorkshire Wolds Gallery
- (i) www.yorkshirewoldsgallery.co.uk
- ☎ 01944 710527

Yorkshire Wolds Railway
- (i) www.yorkshirewoldsrailway.org.uk
- ☎ 01377 338053

Youth Hostel Association
- (i) www.yha.org.uk
- ✎ customerservices@yha.org.uk
- ☎ 0800 019 1700

Further reading

The following gives a broad range of titles about the Yorkshire Wolds. Those books that are out of print may be available through public libraries or online booksellers.

General

Denton, Mark, *The Yorkshire Moors and Wolds*, Frances Lincoln, 2007

Mather, John R., *Where to Watch Birds in Yorkshire: Including the Former North Humberside*, Christopher Helm, 2008

Pevsner, Nikolaus, *Buildings of England. Yorkshire: York and the East Riding*, Yale University Press, 2002

The Rough Guide to Yorkshire, Rough Guides 2011

Vale of York & the Yorkshire Wolds: Pathfinder Guide to shorter walks, Crimson Publishing, 2009

Philip Larkin

The Whitsun Weddings, Faber & Faber, 1964

The Less Deceived, Faber & Faber, 1955

High Windows, Faber & Faber, 1974

Collected Poems, Faber & Faber, 2003

Sunday Sessions, Faber & Faber, 2009

Hartley, Dr Jean, *Philip Larkin's Hull and East Yorkshire*, Philip Larkin Society, 1995

Motion, Andrew, *Philip Larkin: A Writer's Life*, Faber & Faber, 2003

Waters, Geoffrey, *The Larkin Trail Sketchbook*, Kingston Press, 2011

David Hockney

Barringer, Tim, and Devaney, Edith, *David Hockney: A Bigger Picture*, Thames and Hudson, 2012

Hockney's Pictures 2006, Thames & Hudson, 2006

Gayford, Martin, *A Bigger Message: Conversations with David Hockney*, Thames & Hudson, 2011

Hockney David, *A Yorkshire Sketchbook*, RSA, 2011

Sykes, Christopher, *Hockney: the Biography*, Century, 2011

Novels

Holtby, Winifred, *Anderby Wold*, Virago Press, 1981

Holtby, Winifred, *South Riding*, Virago Press, 1996

OS Maps covering Yorkshire Wolds Way

Four maps in the Explorer (1:25 000) series cover the whole of the Yorkshire Wolds Way:

293 Kingston upon Hull & Beverley
294 Market Weighton & Yorkshire Wolds Central
300 Howardian Hills & Malton
301 Scarborough, Bridlington & Flamborough Head

The Ordnance Survey Road Map No. 4 'Northern England', on a scale of 1 inch to 4 miles (1 cm to 2.5km), is useful for reaching the Wolds from further afield.

YWW Official Completion Book

Walkers who like to record the completion of their walk can sign the Completion Book at either the Country Park Stores at Filey Country Park, close to the finish of the route, or at the Tourist Information Centre on John Street in Filey town centre.

The Official Guides to all o

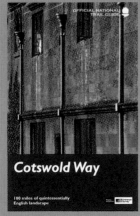

Cotswold Way

100 miles of quintessentially
English landscape

ISBN 978 1 84513 785 4

Cleveland Way

Over 100 miles of magnificent
walking on the North York Moors

ISBN 978 1 84513 781 6

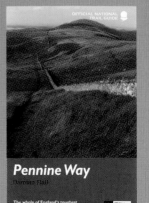

Pennine Way

Damian Hall

The whole of England's toughest
National Trail

ISBN 978 1 84513 718 2

Yorkshire Wolds Way

Roger Ratcliffe

A superbly tranquil walk through
the unspoilt chalk hills of Yorkshire

ISBN 978 178131 064 9

Pembrokeshire Coast Path

Wales Coast Path: St Dogmaels to Amroth

Brian John

ISBN 978 1 84513 782 3

South Downs Way

Paul Millmore

100 miles of glorious chalk downland
for the walker, cyclist and horse rider

ISBN 978 1 78131 088 5

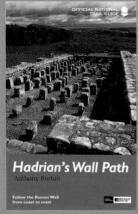

Hadrian's Wall Path

Anthony Burton

Follow the Roman Wall
from coast to coast

ISBN 978 1 84513 808 0

The Ridgeway

87 miles of downland walking
from Wiltshire to the Chilterns

ISBN 978 178131 063 2

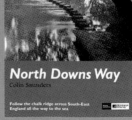

North Downs Way

Colin Saunders

Follow the chalk ridge across South-East
England all the way to the sea

ISBN 978 178131 061 8

Britain's National Trails

Thames Path
in the Country
David Sharp with Tony Gowers
From the source to Hampton Court

ISBN 978 1 84513 717 5

Thames Path
in London
From Hampton Court to Crayford Ness:
50 miles of historic riverside walk

ISBN 978 1 84513 706 9

Peddars Way and
Norfolk Coast Path
Bruce Robinson with Mike Robinson
90 miles from Breckland to
salt marsh and sea cliffs

ISBN 978 1 84513 784 7

South West Coast Path
Minehead to Padstow
Roland Tarr
160 miles of coastal walking from
Exmoor to North Cornwall

ISBN 978 178131 060 1

South West Coast Path
Padstow to Falmouth
John Macadam
From golden beaches to rugged coves
around Britain's southernmost tip

ISBN 978 178131 062 5

Offa's Dyke Path
SOUTH: Chepstow to Knighton
Ernie and Kathy Kay and Mark Richards
Follow the ancient earthwork up the Wye
Valley and alongside the Black Mountains

ISBN 978 1 84513 561 4

South West Coast Path
Falmouth to Exmouth
Brian Le Messurier
172 miles of dramatic coves, cliffs and
beaches from Cornwall to Devon

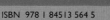

ISBN 978 1 84513 564 5

South West Coast Path
Exmouth to Poole
Roland Tarr
From Jane Austen's Cobb to Lulworth Cove
– over 100 miles of historic coastline

ISBN 978 178131 058 8

NATIONAL TRAIL GUIDES
OFFA'S DYKE PATH NORTH
Knighton to Prestatyn
Ernie and Kathy Kay and Mark Richards

100 miles of walking through the
beautiful Welsh marches

ISBN 978 1 84513 312 2

NATIONAL TRAIL GUIDES
PENNINE BRIDLEWAY
Derbyshire to the
South Pennines
Sue Viccars

ISBN 1 85410 957 X

Other guide books from Aurum

The Capital Ring
Colin Saunders

78 miles of green corridor
encircling inner London

ISBN 978 1 84513 786 1

The London Loop
David Sharp with Colin Saunders

140 miles of secret countryside to walk
in a green corridor around London

ISBN 978 1 84513 787 8

West Highland Way
Anthony Burton

94 miles of Scottish moor and
mountain in Britain's most
spectacular long-distance walk

ISBN 978 178131 089 2

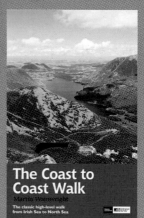

The Coast to Coast Walk
Martin Wainwright

The classic high-level walk
from Irish Sea to North Sea

ISBN 978 1 84513 854 7

Northumberland Coast Path
Roland Tarr

From the centre of Newcastle
to the Scottish border

ISBN 978 178131 056 6

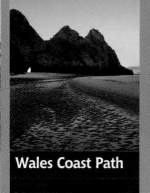

Wales Coast Path

Endless sandy beaches and the
beautiful Gower Peninsula

ISBN 978 178131 067 0

Camino de Santiago
Sergi Ramis

The ancient Way of Saint James pilgrimage route from
the French Pyrenees to Santiago de Compostela

ISBN 978 1 84513 708 3

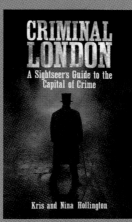

CRIMINAL LONDON
A Sightseer's Guide to the
Capital of Crime

Kris and Nina Hollington

ISBN 978 1 84513 778 6

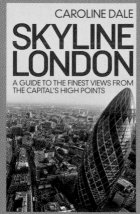

CAROLINE DALE

SKYLINE LONDON
A GUIDE TO THE FINEST VIEWS FROM
THE CAPITAL'S HIGH POINTS

ISBN 978 1 84513 762 5